REPAIRING SMALL ELECTRICAL APPLIANCES

Robert Hertzberg

New York

Published by ARCO PUBLISHING COMPANY, Inc.
219 Park Avenue South, New York, N.Y. 10003

Second Printing, 1969
Library of Congress Catalog Number 68-31702

SBN 668-01810-0

Printed in U.S.A.

CONTENTS

THE REPAIR PROBLEM

It's not really a problem if you can obtain those vital replacement parts.

Housewife Liz Gardner, below, shows off the new line of Proctor-Silex "Lifelong" appliances, which are easily disassembled and assembled without tools. Part go bad? Snap it out, snap in a replacement!

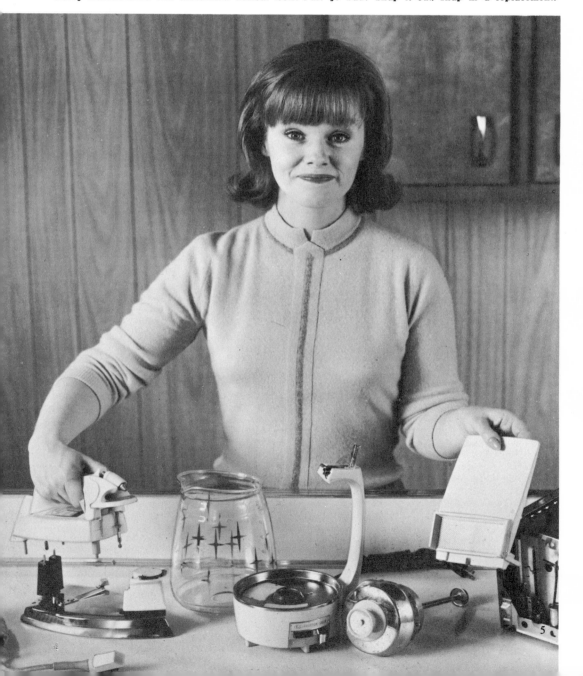

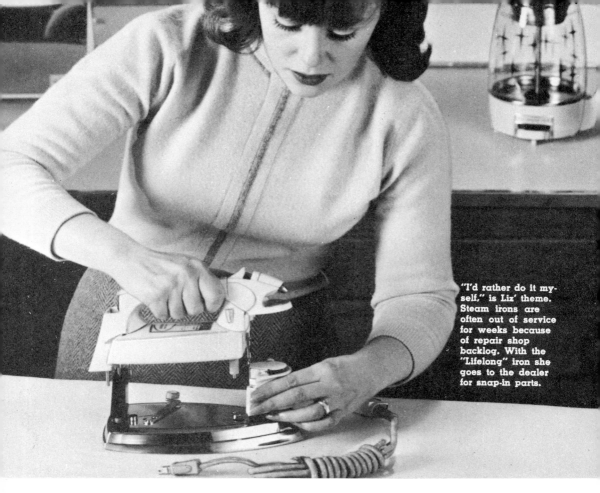

A WOMAN enters a housewares store with a small package under her arm and opens it after being greeted by a clerk.

"I bought this toaster here a couple of years ago," she says. "It seems to have stopped working. Can you fix it?"

The clerk looks into the appliance, jiggles the levers a couple of times, and then assumes a slightly pained expression. "It's burned out all right. This is a discontinued model and we don't have parts for it. However, we can send it to the factory for repair."

"How long will that take?" says the woman.

"Oh, usually about five or six weeks," he replies. "At this time of the year it might be a little longer."

"Five or six weeks! That's terrible!"

"Well, madame, we really can't help it. May I suggest that you consider a new toaster instead? It won't cost much more than the repairs and there's no waiting."

This condensed little story is representative of numerous similar episodes that occur annually in the United States. Consumers have long had the impression that obsolescence is built into many appliances at the factory and that some manufacturers deliberately discourage repair by making replacement parts difficult to obtain. Some firms go even further; by riveting or welding some assemblies they make it virtually impossible just to open an appliance without, in effect, destroying it.

This attitude is particularly puzzling in view of the completely opposite policies of the radio-TV and automobile industries, to take just two examples. There are thousands of full-time and spare-time electronic service technicians scattered around the country who can make repairs either directly in the home or in their own nearby shops. People who have learned the do-it-yourself routine can find self-service tube testers in drug stores, supermarkets and other disparate places and can buy replacement tubes, batteries and some other components in them. There are countless radio dealers, and there is even a large

chain whose name, "Parts, Unlimited," describes its business accurately.

There are gas stations and garages at every crossroads, of course, and even more auto parts stores than radio dealers. The national mail-order firms supply everything from valve caps to complete engines, for cars first produced 40 years ago as well as for more recent ones!

There are encouraging signs that the electrical industry is reforming. Just as this book was being prepared, "Lifelong" household appliances that feature an original and exclusive concept in self-serviceability—a spray/steam/dry iron, a toaster, and an automatic glass percolator—were introduced by Proctor-Silex. Long favorably known for the quality of its products, this firm is a subsidiary of SCM Corporation.

The "Lifelong" line eliminates the problem of having urgently needed household electric equipment out of use while undergoing lengthy repair shop service, when that service is available at all.

The new development reflects adaptation of the modular concept to small electric housewares. Each appliance is made of basic components that can be readily disassembled and re-assembled *in the home without tools*. Get that, *without tools!* Should trouble develop, even a housewife can locate it by following the simplified instruction manual that comes with the device, and she can obtain the needed replacement part immediately from the same dealer who sold her the appliance. This plan supplements but does not replace the company's standard one-year guarantee against mechanical or electrical defects in its brand-name products.

The "Lifelong" appliances are well designed and the cost of the parts is reasonable. For instance, the iron is priced at $16.95 and breaks down to five modular components with tags from $1.50 for the fabric-plate selector to $6.95 for the Teflon coated soleplate. The toaster costs $12.95 and has six elements from 50 cents for the crumb tray to $4.95 for the chassis. The percolator retails for $17.95 and has seven components from $1.00 for the detachable cord to $4.95 for the base with the built-in heating unit. Since the latter is the part most likely to give out after extended use, a repair for less than one-third of the new cost is well worth a trip to the dealer.

When you go shopping for appliances it

Look of a lifetime. Here's an appliance that never has to be left at a shop for repair. This "Lifelong" percolator is made of a few components, all of which are available separately for replacement.

is just as important to pick the right dealer as the best product. If you're interested in an iron, ask him pointedly. "Do you keep replacement heating elements in stock?" This is a fair question because these elements do burn out. If he says, "No, but I can get them," he might mean well, but it might take a month for a new one to reach him. That leaves you with the choice of being without an iron for that period or buying, or possibly borrowing, another one.

Then there's the often overlooked matter of the guarantee. Usually this is printed in tiny type on the packing box or the label of an appliance, and few people bother to read it until something goes wrong. Then they might discover that it is the manufacturer who makes the guarantee, not the dealer, and they might have to go to the nuisance and expense of sending the product to some distant service shop or to the factory itself.

Some of the big merchandising organizations such as Sears, Roebuck & Company, with stores everywhere as well as mail facilities, have met the appliance repair problem to the satisfaction of their customers not only with meaningful guarantees but also with full cooperation in furnishing parts. The Sears motto is "We service what we sell," but in addition to its numerous service centers it also encourages people to buy parts and to make all possible repairs themselves. Of course, this is very smart business, because the firm has the customer coming in not only for the original appliance and parts for it, but also for tools with which to do the work. And it makes a friend of the customer, who returns again and again for other kinds of merchandise.

Some practical suggestions on taking care of and repairing common small household appliances are given in this book. Proper maintenance on a regular basis will in many cases make repairs unnecessary or as a minimum it will greatly prolong the life of a device. You wouldn't dream of letting the oil in the crankcase of your car go down to the empty mark; you undoubtedly check the dip stick once a week or so, and add some oil when needed. With an appliance like a vacuum cleaner, for instance, you can do a similar job by emptying the dirt bag regularly, checking the motor brushes, tightening connections, etc.

Many of the small parts you might need

for appliance repair are simple hardware items that you either already have in your basement or garage shop or that you can buy readily at local stores: such things as nuts, bolts and washers; insulating tape; line cords and plugs; solder and soldering connectors; pilot lights; bulbs of various shapes and sizes; coils of heating wire; etc.

If you need a particular component for a particular appliance, you should start by inquiring at nearby hardware or electrical supply stores. If a "Yellow-Pages" classified directory is published for your area, look under both these categories and do some telephoning. First inquire about the part, and if the answer is negative ask the salesman if he can refer you either to another store or to the nearest factory authorized service station for your make of appliance.

If you didn't save the box in which the device was packed, examine its body closely. Usually the name and address of the manufacturer, the electrical characteristics, the patent numbers, and similar data are stamped on the bottom. Write a letter to the service department of the firm, explain your problem, and ask if they can help. You can expect one of the following things to happen:

1. Nothing. Just plain nothing. That is, the manufacturer, if he's still in business and your letter isn't returned by the post office, will simply ignore it.

2. The letter will be returned by the post office, marked "Unknown at this address" or "Moved. Left no forwarding address."

3. The manufacturer will send back a form letter advising you that your particular appliance is no longer in production and that no replacement parts for it are available. The gadget might be only two years old, but remember, the obsolescence rate of appliances is very high.

4. The manufacturer will send you a list of his authorized service stations and tell you to contact the nearest one.

5. The manufacturer will send you a price list and an order blank and will tell you cheerfully that he'll be glad to send you anything you want.

If your answer is No. 5 you're really in luck. If it's No. 4 you have a fighting chance to get your appliance fixed, even if this takes a couple of months. If the answer is No. 1, No. 2 or No. 3, salvage everything that's removable from the device, throw the rest of it away and go out and buy a new one from a firm that values your good will and wants to keep you as a customer who will pass the good word around to his friends. •

TOOLS FOR THE JOB

You need a lot of small ones, but they don't cost much and last a long time.

Even if you start fresh and have to buy all your tools new, you will find that they aren't expensive. Get the very top grade; they are definitely cheaper in the long run than imported "bargains."

THE maintenance and repair of household electrical appliances can be done readily with the aid of common hand tools such as those used for other house chores, for car work, for adjustment of lawn mowers and snow blowers, etc. In fact, anything that cannot be done with hand tools usually cannot be done at all at home, or for that matter even in so-called professional shops.

Consider the jobs that need doing: nuts and bolts to be removed or installed; wood and self-tapping screws to be taken out and put in; wires to be cut, cleaned, soldered and taped; plugs to be repaired or replaced; open and short-circuits to be identified, isolated and rectified; burned out fuses and heating elements to be replaced; noisy motors to be silenced, etc.

Sometimes a three-second application of a soldering gun to a broken connection restores a previously dead appliance to full working condition; or tightening a few screws on a grill puts the heating wires back into proper position and eliminates dangerous sparking; or a half-turn with a wrench cures a leak in a blender or coffee pot. Sometimes you can even affect a "repair" without any tools; for example, a noisy electric clock can usually be silenced if you merely turn it upside down and then

let it run that way for a couple of hours!

If you're new at the game of doing things around the house yourself—a role forced on virtually all men because of the cost and incompetence of "professionals" —you will learn by visiting any hardware store that tools are plentiful and inexpensive. Used properly, they will last a very long time and are therefore good investments.

Avoid cheap tools made in the Orient. They are cheap in quality as well as cost, and do not compare with American-made products in either finish or durability.

Pliers for Cutting and Holding

As a minimum, there should be three pairs of pliers in every tool box. The first is a 5-inch pair of side-cutters. The only function of this tool is to snip copper wire up to and including No. 18, the size commonly used as lamp cord. It has two ground edges about ⅞ inch long, very accurately fitted so that they cut well right up to their tips. This enables you to trim thin individual strands of flexible wire from under terminal screws and soldered joints, where they might otherwise cause trouble by touching other live contact surfaces. An easy way to ruin a good pair of side-cutters is to use them for slitting sheet metal or for loosening or tightening nuts and bolts. Reserve them strictly for wire cutting and they'll last practically forever.

The second tool is a 6-inch pair of what is called "electrician's pliers." Of much heavier construction than side-cutters, these have square jaws about ⅜ inch wide, with serrated inner surfaces for gripping bolt heads, nuts, bars, rods, wire and anything else up to about ¾ inch wide or in diameter. Except for the fact that the jaws

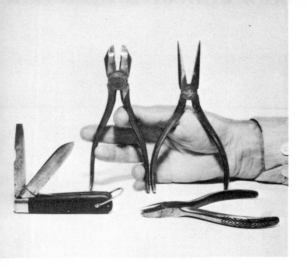

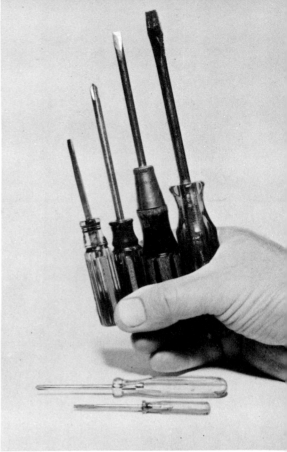

Standing, left to right: Army surplus screwdriver/knife combination; electrician's pliers; longnose pliers. Front: side-cutters, intended only for wire. These tools are handy for many purposes.

No one ever has enough screwdrivers, but this typical assortment takes care of most small electrical appliances. It includes drivers for Phillips head screws and conventional straight-slot types.

Box, left, holds small sockets and several handles for them. The nut drivers, right, are built like screwdrivers and do same job. The adjustable jaw wrench, center, is fine for occasional large nuts.

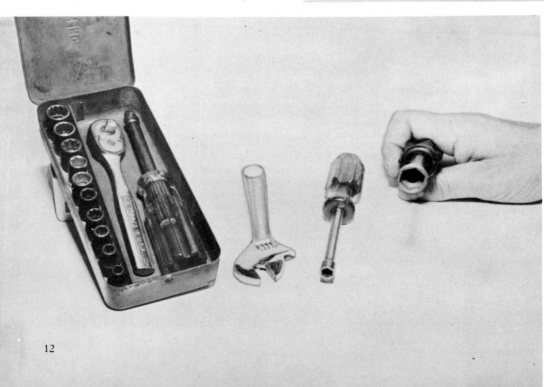

don't lock, this tool is virtually a small hand vise.

Between the jaws and the center hinge of the electrician's pliers is a pair of ground edges suitable for cutting wire of any size likely to be found in a home electric system. Formed into these edges are two pairs of half holes, which are very useful for trimming off the insulation on wires without nipping into the wire itself. After some experimenting on scrap pieces of wire you will know just how much squeezing pressure to put on the handles to sever different thicknesses of insulation on different diameters of wire.

The third pair of pliers is called "long-nose" because that's just what they look like. A handy size is 6½ inches long. The nose, which consists actually of two matching sections, tapers down almost but not quite to a point. The inside surfaces are flat, without cutting edges. The long-nose is intended strictly for light work, such as twisting wires around terminals, holding nuts while screws are being started into them, holding wires that are being soldered, etc. The flat inner surfaces can also be used for bending or forming *thin* sheet metal. Do *not* use the tool for loosening

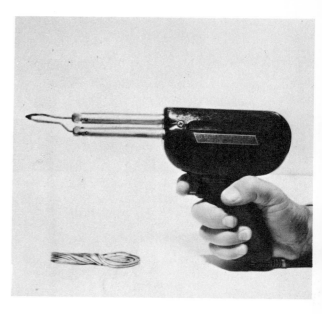

It looks like a pistol and it even has a trigger, but this is only a soldering "gun," probably the most important single tool in electrical repairs. The replaceable wire tip, left, is what gets hot.

You may have to cut or drill your way into some appliances, so the hack saw and drill (top) are necessary tools. Scissors for cutting tape and insulation and the arc-joint pliers are also of value.

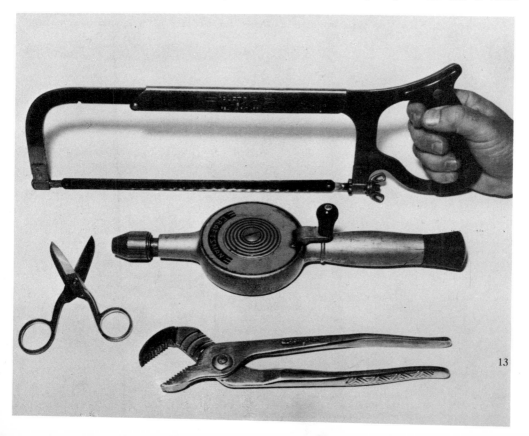

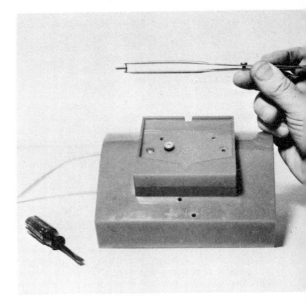

Socket wrenches such as those used in automobile work are indispensable for reaching some large nuts in recessed spaces, as in this drink blender. Arc-joint pliers are sometimes suitable too.

Locking type tweezers save much time and temper in retrieving small parts and in helping to put them back into position. They can securely hold even the thinnest screws, nuts, washers, lugs, etc.

It is often helpful to supplement the soldering gun (center) with a small soldering iron of the pencil type (bottom), for which variety of screw-in tips is available. Hammer and file are other good tools.

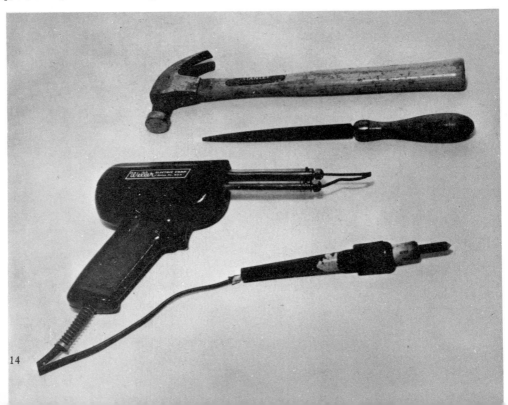

tight nuts or tightening loose ones; these are jobs for the electrician's pliers or a wrench.

Screwdrivers, Plain and Fancy

Conventional screws have straight slots in their heads, and screwdrivers to fit them therefore have blades with flat ends. However, manufacturers of appliances tend to favor the Phillips type of screw. In this, the heads are formed with two slots at right angles to each other and with slightly rounded bottoms, and they therefore require special screwdrivers with tips of mating shape. Why do manufacturers prefer this type over the simpler straight-slot kind? Because it lends itself better to fast assembly with air or motor driven tools. A Phillips bit centers itself almost automatically in the opening in the screw head and once in does not slip out.

Screwdrivers are cheap because they are simple tools. For the small screws found in most appliances you need at least three of both the flat and Phillips types, but you'll undoubtedly acquire more. There is considerable latitude in fitting flat blades to ordinary screws, but for Phillips screws you must have the exact size or you will mash the openings. In a pinch, if a Phillips isn't too tight, you can loosen it with a flat blade that enters one slot, but this takes careful twisting.

Nut Drivers and Wrenches

Another very useful small tool looks like a screwdriver but is actually in the wrench family. Called a "nut driver," it has the handle and the shaft of a screwdriver and the end of a socket wrench. The shaft is hollow for about half its length, so it can be slipped over the end of a long screw to reach a nut on it. Of course, you need a size for every nut. For electrical work the ¼-inch and 5/16-inch models are usually enough.

For larger nuts and bolts you have a wide choice of adjustable jaw wrenches or socket wrenches. A boxed assortment of sockets from 3/16 to ¾ inch, with ratchet, straight and angled handles, is very popular.

Two tools that look like pliers also are in the wrench family. One is called "arc-joint pliers" and has jaws that stay more or less parallel as their spacing is adjusted in five or six steps. The other is called "slip-joint pliers" and has slightly concave jaws that are adjustable to two positions. In some parts of the country this type is called "gas pliers" because at one time they were used extensively for tightening gas pipes and other round fittings.

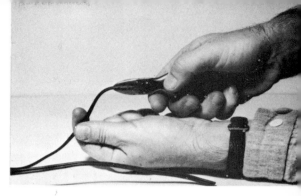

This picture and the nine following show steps in common job of extending a line cord and soldering the joints in it. First operation is to use side-cutters and to open all ends of wire about an inch.

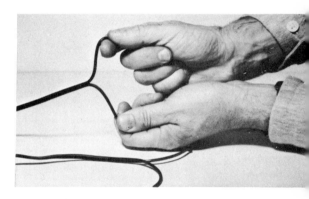

Now grasp the ends and pull them apart for length of about six inches. This works fine with "zip" cords, but with other types of wire you may have to ease the insulation apart with a sharp knife.

With side-cutters cut one wire in each pair back about four inches. Using a sharp knife, pare off about two inches of insulation on each. Mate the shorts with longs for joints that do not overlap.

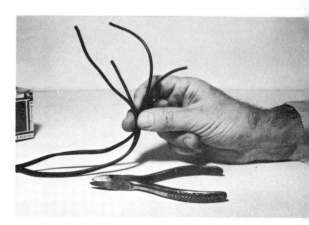

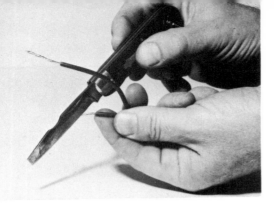

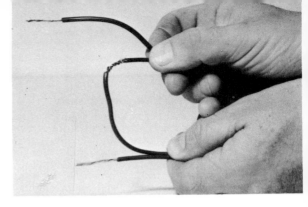

If wires are not already "tinned" (coating during manufacture with thin coating of solder) scrape them bright and clean with back edge of a knife. Keep fingers off wires, to maintain cleanliness.

Take the long wire of one cord and the short one of the other, cross the bared ends and twist together, using pliers as much as possible instead of fingers. Renew surface by more light scraping.

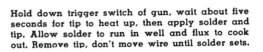

Hold down trigger switch of gun, wait about five seconds for tip to heat up, then apply solder and tip. Allow solder to run in well and flux to cook out. Remove tip, don't move wire until solder sets.

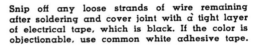

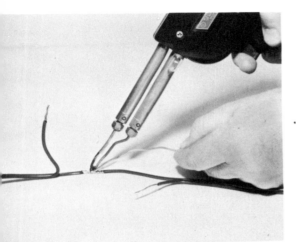

Snip off any loose strands of wire remaining after soldering and cover joint with a tight layer of electrical tape, which is black. If the color is objectionable, use common white adhesive tape.

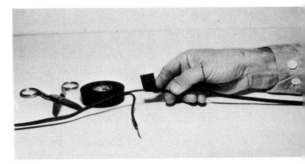

Make another twisted joint of the remaining two wires of the extended cord. Separate them slightly so that the hot tip of the gun does not burn adjacent tape. Snip off any loose strands of wire.

Put a layer of tape over the second joint, press the two wires together, and put a final second layer over them. Run this tape about an inch beyond the first layers and press it down firmly.

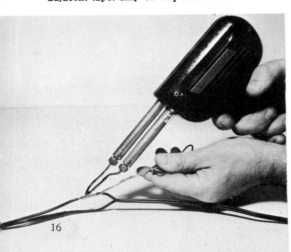

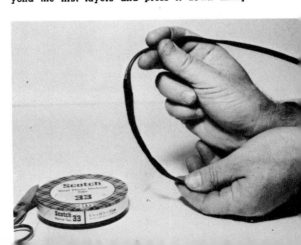

Miscellaneous Tools

A common hack saw is always useful for cutting bolts, metal bars and rods. A small hand or power drill is a necessity for making holes. A pair of scissors is for cutting tape and trimming insulation. A husky pocketknife of the Boy Scout type is for paring off insulation and scraping wires.

A pair of tweezers can't be beat for picking up, holding or retrieving small screws, nuts, washers, etc. A simple one of the kind used for cosmetic purposes, holding stamps, etc., will serve the purpose, but a better one, sold by radio supply houses, has a locking feature. This is of great help when you have to position a small part accurately.

One flat and one round file, of medium grade, are invaluable for removing burrs and similar rough edges from the metal cases or bodies of some appliances. A small round file, usually called a "rattail," will enlarge screw holes, a necessary job sometimes when a disassembled appliance twists out of shape slightly and the original holes don't match.

The Soldering Operation

Soldering is a very important process in all electrical and radio work, because loose or broken wires in appliances of all kinds are very common. Lots of people have trouble with it, only for a single, simple reason: the metal surfaces they try to join are not clean and bright. Sometimes they do scrape wires and terminal lugs until they shine, but then they pick them up with their fingers and deposit a thin film of body oil on them. Molten solder is almost like water in that it will not stick to a dirty surface, especially a greasy one.

The most popular soldering tool these days is not an "iron" but a "gun." The older iron type, still indispensable for many purposes, is not an iron at all. Its tip, which does the work, is made of copper, and it is heated by a coil of resistance wire in its base. The gun type, so called because of its obvious resemblance to an auto-loading pistol, works differently. Its tip is actually a U-shaped loop of thick copper wire, usually of square cross-section, which forms part of a single-turn secondary of a transformer. The primary coil of this transformer, consisting of about 150 turns of fine wire, is in the body of the gun. It is connected to the AC house line through a trigger switch.

In a transformer, the voltage developed in the secondary is directly proportional to the turns ratio of the primary and secondary windings. In the case of a soldering gun plugged into a 115-volt line, the voltage across the one-turn secondary is thus only a fraction of one volt. Because the wire tip has a low resistance, even this low voltage pushes a lot of amperes through it, and it gets hot enough to melt solder.

Although most guns are top-heavy and at first a bit awkward to handle, they have these important features: they come up to melting temperature in several seconds; they cool off quickly; the tips last a long time and are cheap and easy to replace; the tips can be bent to reach into very tight wiring that would surely be damaged by an iron with its bigger end.

The solder universally used for electrical work is a 50/50 mixture of lead and tin, formed as soft tubing filled with resin. The latter is called "flux." Its job is to absorb the slight products of oxidation resulting from the application of the hot tip of the soldering tool to the joint being soldered. Without flux, hot solder simply rolls away.

The technique in soldering wire joints and other connections is to hold the solder over the joint and the tip over the solder, and to let the latter melt its way into the joint while the resin cooks and smokes. The flux has an odor faintly reminiscent of turpentine, of which it is a derivative. Keep the iron in position for several seconds, or until the resin stops smoking. Then remove it *without disturbing the joint*. Watch the latter closely and you will see that it takes another few seconds to change color and finally harden.

Many people tend to remove the heat too soon. The usual result is that the flux rehardens on the joint, and instead of helping the solder to mate with the wires it actually prevents it from doing so. Under close inspection a joint can appear to be perfectly normal, yet even with testers as simple as the Clicktester and the VOM (see pages 18 and 22) it will prove, unbelievably, to be absolutely open.

Fortunately, copper takes to solder very well; soldered copper wire joints are strong both physically and electrically. Brass, which is an alloy of copper and zinc, also reacts very favorably. Iron is more stubborn. It needs not only a very hot iron but also a more virulent flux, usually acid in nature. Aluminum is almost hopeless. The easy way to make an electrical connection to iron or aluminum is to solder the copper wire to a copper lug of some sort and to bolt the lug securely to the metal. •

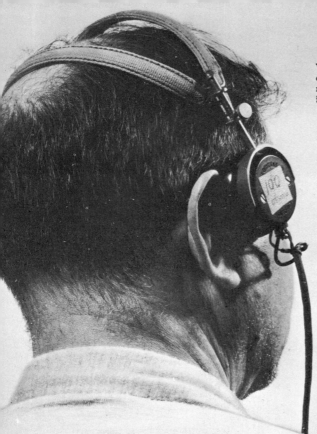

When used with certain appliances such as small clocks, can openers, etc., sound from Clicktester may be weak. To make sure you're not missing it, wear phones close to ears or directly on 'em.

Inexpensive and easy to make, it "shoots" many common electrical troubles.

THE CLICKTESTER

A flashlight cell of any size, double earphones or a single earphone, a terminal strip, a length of flexible wire and two "alligator" clips are all you need. Cost, little more than one dollar!

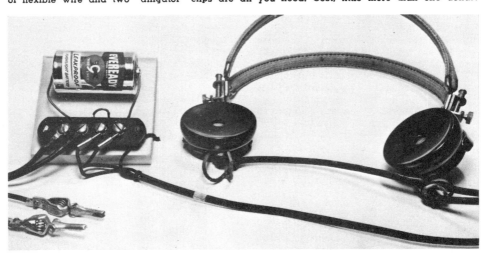

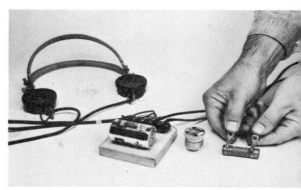

Common switch illustrates basic continuity test possible with the Clicktester. Switch contacts closed, loud click from earphones when clips are applied. Switch contacts open, nothing is heard.

Is suspected resistor burned out or still intact? Is normal looking fuse really normal, or is wire inside melted through? Clickester gives answers in an instant. Clicks, they're OK. Otherwise, NG.

Flexible cords used with many appliances suffer internal damage from mere physical abuse. To test for possible short circuit, leave one plug alone, connect Clicktester to other. No noise, no short.

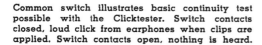

PRACTICALLY all small electrical appliances contain wire in one form or another. In toasters, irons, broilers, etc., it normally becomes red hot to make the device perform its intended function. In mixers, fans, electric knives, etc., the wire is in the form of coils which produce electromagnetism for motor operation. These motor windings normally become warm after prolonged running, but not hot enough to burn.

Machines of all types are turned on and off by switches which consist merely of a short piece of copper moving against or across one or more fixed contacts.

The two most common troubles that develop in any appliance are "open circuits," due to actual burn-outs of the wires that carry current, and "short circuits," which represent accidental connections between points that should not be connected. Fortunately, it is rather easy to check these conditions with the aid of a very simple tester that you put together in minutes. This is called the "Clicktester" because it gives an audible signal.

The device consists merely of a single flashlight cell, of the penlight, "C" or "D" size; two pieces of flexible insulated wire about two feet long, fitted with "alligator" spring clips at one end; a single or double telephone receiver; a wood baseboard about four inches square; and a four-screw terminal strip. A scrap piece of lamp cord is fine for the test leads if you

Maybe no short, but also maybe a broken internal wire. Leave Clicktester connected to prongs of line plug, short other plug with tweezers, hairpin, etc. Clicks, cord OK. No clicks, cord open.

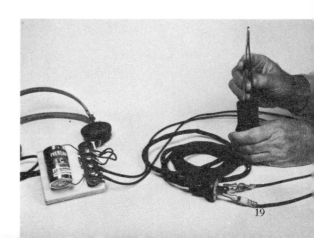

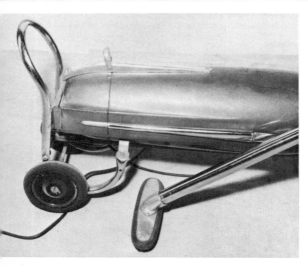

This is how appliance cords become damaged. They are cut up by the sharp edges of irons, run over by vacuum cleaners, stepped on, used as skipping ropes by kids, etc. Care saves burnouts.

Clicktester is great for making quick and positive test on metal cased appliances for possible connection—DANGEROUS—between case and line cord. Turn on appliance switch to close circuit.

separate the two wires from the outer covering of cotton insulation. A telephone receiver of any type, size or shape whatsoever serves the purpose. You can buy one of the hearing aid style for as little as 69 cents, new; or a single phone with a headband for about $1.30. From the early days of radio there are still thousands of perfectly good double headsets gathering dust in attics and cellars, just waiting for a useful application like the Clicktester.

The idea is to connect the battery, the earphone and the test leads in simple series. The baseboard and the terminal strip make the unit easy to move around. There are clip mounts for single dry cells, but soldering a couple of short wires to the battery is less work.

No Danger from Shock

With the test leads separated, the earphone is silent. Touch the clips together, or place them both on a nail or other short piece of metal, and the phone will click loudly once as you make the contact and once as you open it. You don't even have to put the phone to your ear if the room is quiet, as the sound is quite sharp. Incidentally, there is absolutely no shock danger whatsoever from the 1½ volts of a single flashlight cell.

If you have a loose switch of any kind in the family's odds-and-ends box, use it for a couple of quick experiments. Touch the test leads to the terminals. If you hear nothing, the switch is probably in its normal open position. Push or turn the handle and again try the leads. If you hear loud clicks, the internal contacts have closed properly. With the leads clipped to the terminals, move the handle back and forth and note the clicking response.

But suppose that you get no sound with the switch handle in either position. This means that it is permanently open, and cannot pass current. Possibly the internal spring has popped out of position, or the switch blade itself is broken. Or suppose that you get a strong click from either handle position. This means that the internal contacts are closed tight, possibly because of a defective spring again, or more likely because they are burned together from some heavy overload.

A similar test with fuses is also illuminating. You can look into a fuse of the common screw-in type (called "plug" fuses in the electrical trade, for some mysterious reason) and tell—most of the time

—whether it is OK or not. However, some cheap fuses can be foolers. Touch one test clip to the tip and the other to the threaded body, and you'll know instantly whether a particular fuse is good or bad.

The cartridge fuses generally used on circuits carrying 30 amperes or more cannot be checked visually, as the fusible element is encased in a fiber tube. The Clicktester quickly reveals a burned-out one by its silence.

Checking Line Cords

Many irons, toasters, broilers, etc., use a line cord that has an ordinary line plug on one end and a large flat plug at the other to fit the appliance itself. If subjected to physical abuse, like being stepped on or chewed up by a cabinet door, these can develop intermittent wire-to-wire "shorts" or "opens." Here again the Clicktester shows its usefulness. To check for possible shorts, hook the test clips to the prongs of the line plug, being careful not to let them touch each other. Now wiggle and flex the entire length of the cord. If the phone remains silent, there are no shorts. If you hear an occasional crackle, the wire is damaged and should be replaced.

To double-check the cord for continuity, leave the clips in place, and now cross-connect the contacts inside the large plug by means of a pair of tweezers or a short piece of wire. Loud clicks as you make and break the contact mean that the cord is OK.

Heat appliances and line cords for all appliances offer relatively little resistance to the flow of electricity, and they allow virtually the full voltage of the flashlight cell to actuate the earphone. However, some small motor-operated devices such as electric clocks contain rather thin wire that has appreciable resistance. The test clicks may be more subdued than before, and you may have to put the phone into or over your ear to hear them. Don't hesitate to experiment with any electrical appliance in the house, to determine approximately what good ones should sound like. You can't possibly damage them with the low voltage of a flashlight cell. Just remember to unplug the appliance before you play with it. You have to anyway, to connect to the line plug!

Various applications of the Clicktester to particular appliances are shown elsewhere in this book. •

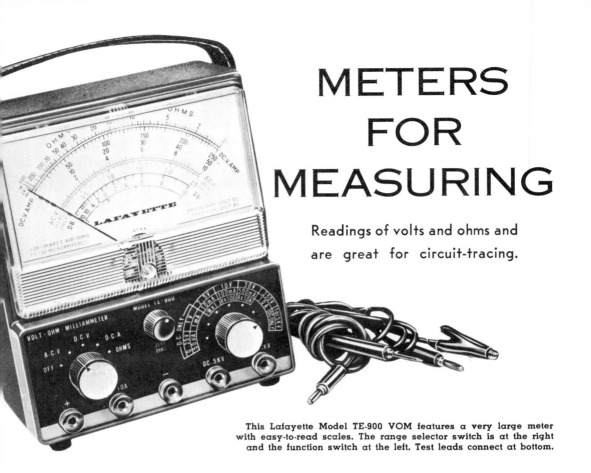

METERS FOR MEASURING

Readings of volts and ohms and are great for circuit-tracing.

This Lafayette Model TE-900 VOM features a very large meter with easy-to-read scales. The range selector switch is at the right and the function switch at the left. Test leads connect at bottom.

FOR SOMEWHAT more sophisticated electrical troubleshooting than can be performed with the Clicktester, many men prefer a very simple but highly versatile instrument universally called the "VOM," pronounced "vee-oh-em." This shows AC and DC voltages (V) and resistance values in ohms (O) on the face of a meter (M). The various functions are selected by a rotary switch. Connections between the meter and the appliance or circuit under test are made by a pair of flexible wires with clips or points on their ends.

Excellent VOM's entirely suitable for electrical work cost as little as $5.00. Better ones that also are applicable to electronic gear, such as radio and television sets, photo equipment, etc., start at about $10. Very often even a $25 VOM pays for itself the first time it isolates and identifies a mysterious fault in an appliance.

Most VOM's can also measure current in terms of amperes or fractions of an ampere. This capability is more of a sales feature than a necessity. To measure voltage or resistance you only need touch the probes to the terminals of a device, without disturbing existing wiring. To measure current you have to open a circuit physically by unsoldering or cutting a wire and connecting the probes to the two ends that thus form. This is a nuisance of a job, and in fact can't be done conveniently or even inconveniently in many appliances. What saves the situation is the fact that if the voltages and resistances in a circuit are normal the current values automatically become so.

Operation of a VOM takes little skill or training. The main trick is to read the correct scale in relation to the setting of the function selector switch. The instruction booklet that comes with every meter explains exactly how to use the resistance ranges for visual "continuity checking" and the voltage ranges for measuring as little as 1½ volts from a flashlight battery to 220 volts from an AC line.

To familiarize yourself with the VOM and to prepare yourself for troubleshooting

When test probes are touched together, or "short circuited," needle swings to zero ohms. If they are connected to appliance in working order, the meter will read the resistance of internal wires.

Typical VOM, a Knight-Kit model. Test probes are insulated handles with metal tips. With selector switch set for "ohms" and probes separated, the meter needle doesn't move, showing open circuit.

There should be no contact between heating wire of bowl heater and metal frame. VOM should show open circuit (no reading) when connected to the frame and to the prongs of the line plug, in turn.

Hooked directly to prongs of line plug, the VOM should show a resistance of about 10 ohms for an iron in normal condition. Lack of any reading is sign that heating element or thermostat is open.

The Simpson Model 260 is a popular factory-made VOM. Ohms scale on face of the meter is at the top; voltage and current ranges below. As in all VOM's batteries for resistance measurement are in the case.

Small fans contain thin wire and usually have a resistance of 20 to 25 ohms, as measured directly at the line plug. Be sure the fan's switch is on for this test! If it isn't, meter reads open.

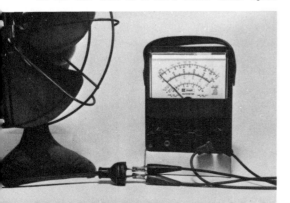

23

The Heathkit MM-1 "Multitester"
or VOM is fine for testing of
electrical appliances and much
electronic equipment. It reads to
fraction of an ohm and even
to as high as 1500 volts DC.

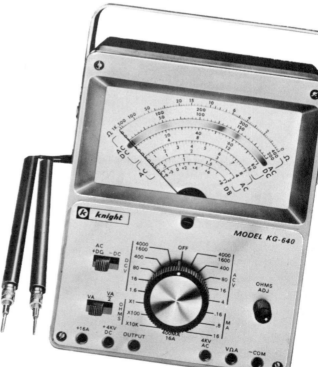

Mirrored scale (between AC-DC
markings) on the Knight KG-640
VOM makes accurate readings
of the needle easy. Can measure
resistance from .2 ohm all the
way to 10 megohms (ten million).

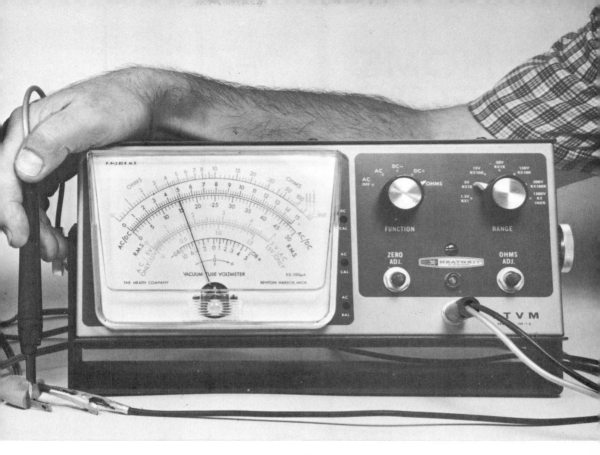

This, above, is a typical test meter of a more advanced type than the VOM. It is a vacuum-tube voltmeter, usually called "VTVM." While intended primarily for electronics, it is also great for appliances.

in the future, it is very instructive to collect a few typical household appliances and to run resistance measurements through their line cords or any accessible metal terminals. Don't forget to snap the control switch on and off a couple of times to be sure of which position is which! Heating devices generally have low resistance; small motor-driven ones run higher. The cold resistance of lamp filaments is also low, although the hot resistance is much higher. Since you can check lamps only when they're cold, the meter needle tells, as a minimum, that the element is intact or open.

The resistance-measuring function of a VOM requires one or two small flashlight cells, which are mounted in clips inside the case of the instrument. Current is delivered only for the few seconds of a test, so the batteries last quite a long time. They need to be inspected once in a while for signs of leakage, and to be replaced when

the meter needle fails to read zero when probes are short-circuited to each other.

One of the quickest things you can do with a VOM, within minutes of unpacking it, is to measure the AC line voltage by setting the function switch to the 300-volt AC range and carefully inserting the test leads into the slots of a wall outlet. If you expect the reading to be "110," the value traditionally associated with AC lines, you may be in for a surprise. Much more likely the reading will be 115, 117, 119, even 120, depending on the time of day, season of the year, and age of the power distribution system. Utility companies all over the country are continually beefing up their generating capacity to take care of air conditioning and electric kitchens, and the trend is definitely toward higher voltages. If the voltage in your home or apartment is consistently below about 112 you should call the local utility and ask to have the service investigated. •

HOME
ELECTRIC
SYSTEM

You can identify its type by number
of wires entering main switch box.

Typical pole transformer in residential district
steps down high voltage from top lines to three-
phase, four-wire service at 120/208 volts. Twisted
wires send this to houses on both sides of street.

MOST people take the power system of
their homes for granted. They know
that all they have to do is flip a switch, and
a mysterious, magical force provides light
when it's dark, heat when it's cold, and
cold when it's hot. Inevitably, however,
there comes a time when flipping a switch
produces only a small noise and nothing
else, and that's when you wish you knew
something about the wiring and everything connected to it.

Practically all commercially produced
electricity in the United States is now "alternating current." This is usually abbre-
viated to AC as a matter of convenience
in both oral and written references. The
great feature of AC is that it can be con-
verted with high efficiency from any voltage to any other voltage, either up or
down, over an unlimited range of ratios.
This is done by devices called "transformers," which have no moving parts,
require little if any maintenance, and last
virtually forever if not overloaded.

The AC "Wave Form"

Figure 1 is the nearest possible graphic
representation of the AC "wave form," or
the way the current flows in a circuit. Let's
follow the action of an alternator in terms
of time and generated voltage. For measuring time we'll use an imaginary stop
watch that reads 1/60 of a second from
start to stop; for showing voltage, a zero
center meter whose needle moves to the
right when current flows in one direction
and to the left when it flows in the opposite
direction.

With the alternator at rest, nothing, of
course, happens. Let's click the stop watch
the instant the machine starts to turn, and
watch the voltmeter. With the first slight
movement of the alternator, electrons in
its wires are agitated and the meter needle
starts to move, let us say to the right. As
the rotation continues, the voltage builds
up proportionately. At 1/240 of a second
after the starting time the voltage reaches
its peak value, and then starts to drop. It
falls back to zero after another 1/240 of
a second, or a total elapsed time of 1/120
second.

As the machine turns, another section
of wires comes into play, and a new voltage
is created just as the first one dies to nothing. It builds up in value exactly as its
predecessor did, but it flows in the *opposite*
direction, as a left-hand deflection of the
voltmeter indicates. At 1/80 second after
the starting time this second voltage
reaches its peak value, which is identical
with that of the first voltage, and then it,
too, starts to decay. It drops to its zero 1/60
second after the starting time.

If we let the alternator run, the process
keeps repeating itself. One complete varia-
tion of current from zero through peak to
zero, and again from zero to peak to zero
the other way, is called a "cycle"; each half
is called an "alternation." The number of
cycles per second (c.p.s.) is called the
"frequency"; in this case 60, which is universally supplied to homes in the United
States.

The alternations of the AC cycle are invariably referred to as "positive" and
"negative." The latter is somewhat mis-
leading in that it infers uselessness. Actually, the two alternations *are absolutely
identical in their ability to do work.*

The Distribution Network

Power is generated in modern stations
at voltages between 11,000 and 14,000. By
means of transformers, this is boosted to
values ranging from 23,000 to as high as

275,000 volts, the higher voltages being used for the longest lines.

As power is needed in various areas, the high voltages are brought to much lower levels by step-down transformers. A primary distribution point or "substation" changes them to between 2500 and 15,000 volts. A secondary distribution point, which may be merely a transformer on a pole or concealed in a vault below street level, brings the power down to the eventual consumer level. In residential areas this is usually either 115 or 230 volts, or both on the same circuit.

The figure "115" is a flexible one. Depending on the age of the power system, the number of houses fed by one transformer, the time of the day, the size of the actual wiring in the individual home, and the number and type of appliances in use at one time, the voltage may vary from 110 to 125. In older residential districts it runs to the low side; in newer ones steady readings of 120, 121 and 122 volts are normal. For purposes of discussion let's use 115 volts to represent all values between 110 and 125, and 230 volts for voltages from about 220 to 240. The figure of 208 volts appears in some cases, but this is a special value, not even related to either 115 or 230. It is taken up later in this section in the discussion of four-wire systems.

The Two-Wire House System

The majority of small houses built prior to the television and electric appliance boom of the post-World War II period are fed with a simple, basic two-wire power system. Two wires, running from the nearest secondary distribution transformer, enter the house. They might be suspended aerially from a pole on the curb line, or they might be completely out of sight in buried pipe. With such a two-wire service, the voltage is always "115." See Figure 2. One wire has white or gray colored insulation. It is connected to the nearest water pipe and is called the "ground" wire. The second wire has black insulation and is called the "hot" side of the line only to distinguish it from the other. The grounded wire is by no means "cold" by implication; the two wires can function only together, not separately.

The main switch and the main fuse are usually in a single steel box. The cover of the latter is linked to the switch handle in such a manner that the fuse is accessible inside only when the switch is thrown to "off." With the switch open or the fuse burned out, the entire electrical system of the house is dead.

The watt-hour meter registers the power consumed in the house. Following it, there are usually several individual "branch" circuits, each with a fuse. These feed power to various parts of the house.

The Three-Wire System

In many areas power is brought into a building by a three-wire, dual-voltage system, as shown in Figure 3. The center wire is called the "neutral," has white or gray insulation, and is grounded. Between this neutral and either outside black wire is the normal 115 volts. The various 115-volt branch circuits are distributed so that each half of the system carries about the same power load.

In most cases the three-wire system is wired only to feed standard 115-volt lamps and appliances. It is a simple matter, however, to obtain a circuit from the two outside black wires alone to give 230 volts, for the operation of an air conditioner, a large freezer, etc. The advantage of using the higher voltage is that the current in amperes is reduced, and this minimizes heat losses in the line. A specific example is standard 1/3 horsepower motor that works equally well on either 115 or 230 volts through a slight shifting of its internal connections. It develops the same 1/3 h.p. in either case and registers the same power on the watt-hour meter. However, while it draws 6 amperes on 115 volts, it takes only 3 on 230 volts.

Three-wire installations are standard in homes having all-electric kitchens. There is usually a separate heavy-duty 230-volt line from the meter directly to the range, which can easily take as much as 50 or 60 amperes even at this higher voltage.

The Four-Wire System

The wave form shown in Figure 1 is a picture of AC as it would be generated in a simple, basic alternator. This is called

Figure 1: AC in action is shown in diagram form; fluctuations produce magnetic effects by means of which voltages can be stepped up or down.

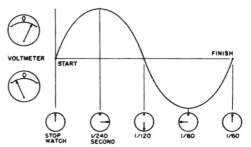

"single phase" power because only one build up of voltage in each direction takes place during the 1/60 second of a complete cycle. In actual practice the large stations do not generate single phase power, but what is called "polyphase" or "three-phase" power. From it single phase circuits are derived as needed.

Until recently polyphase power was used exclusively for industrial purposes where motors of one horsepower or more constituted the major part of the load. With the increasing use of central air conditioning in the home, the power companies are putting polyphase circuits into many new residential districts. These conditioners run to 2, 3, 5 and even more horsepower, and represent little "industrial" installations all by themselves.

Look at Figure 4. The wave form or curve marked A is the same as that of Figure 1. It represents the voltage developed by one set of windings in the rotating alternator. As before, the first alternation is completed in 1/120 second, the complete cycle in 1/60 second. In an actual machine, there is not one but three sets of identical windings, separated 120 degrees or ⅓ of a revolution. As the alternator starts to turn from its theoretical dead starting point, the first winding starts to generate the voltage A and continues to do so as the motion continues. A scant 1/180 second after the starting time, the second winding comes into play and generates the voltage B, which is exactly like A. While voltage A is building up the second alternation of its first cycle, the third winding comes into play at the 1/90 second point, and generates the voltage C. This is a replica of its predecessors A and B. With the alternator turning over steadily, power is delivered THREE times during each cycle of 1/60 second duration, instead of only once. For motor operation, three-phase supply has the same advantage over single-phase supply that multiple-cylinder gasoline engines have over single-cylinder jobs.

Figure 2 shows basic hook-up of two-wire power distribution generally found in older residences.

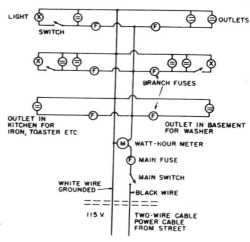

Figure 3 shows basic three-wire system, which makes both 115 and 230 volts available in house.

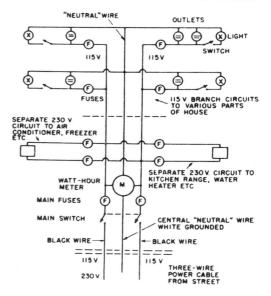

Figure 4: Three-phase power generated by most large generating stations. Curves A, B, C are of three separate voltages which flow in same circuit 1/180-second apart. This type is for large motor operation.

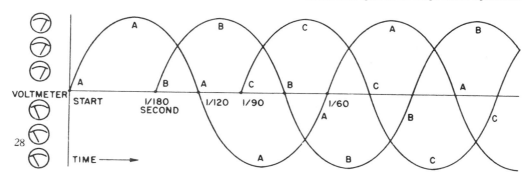

As it reaches the home, three-phase power takes the form of a *four*-wire cable from the street. People with some practical knowledge of electricity and radio are invariably confused by this wiring the first time they see it. They usually know about three-wire, 230-volt service, but they can't figure the four. The arrangement is really quite simple. See Figure 5. One of the wires again has white insulation, and as you might expect by now, is the grounded neutral. All the other three wires have red covering. Between the ground wire and *each* of the red wires you pick off 120-volt *single*-phase power for the usual "115-volt" household machines and appliances. Each branch circuit has its own fuse. The big air-conditioner motor, a three-phase unit, is connected by three leads to the three *red* wires only, through its own set of three fuses. Because of the tricky interweaving of the three phase voltages, a separate return or neutral wire is not needed with a motor load. The voltage between any two red wires of the three-phase circuit is 208 volts; repeat: 208 volts, NOT 230 or 240.

Three-Wire, 208-Volt System

In some residential districts of some of the major cities of the United States, the *only* power distribution system is of the four-wire, three-phase type previously described. The conventional 115/230-volt, three-wire system might not be available at all. A builder of medium-priced homes, which do not have central air conditioning as original equipment, might not elect to bring the full four-wire service into them, Instead, he will ask for basic "115-volt" service, and let the buyers of the houses worry about the operation of air conditioners, driers, etc., that they might buy later.

Actually, what the power companies then install is *three*-wire service from the *four*-wire facilities on their street poles. One wire is the usual common ground; the other two are random pairs of the outside "phase legs." Neighboring houses are on staggered legs, so that the load is distributed over the wires and not concentrated on any one pair. See Figure 6.

Between the ground and *either* phase leg the voltage is a full 120, and this is led through the house to operate the usual "115-volt" lamps and appliances. Again, the lines are staggered between the common ground and the two phase wires, to distribute the load.

Now comes the joker: *The voltage across the two outside wires is not 240 volts, as it*

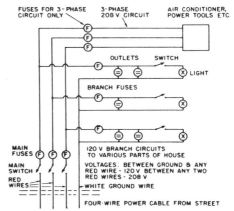

Figure 5: Basic four-wire, three-phase power system, with the watt-hour meter omitted for the sake of simplicity. The 115-volt circuits displayed here are distributed between ground and red wires.

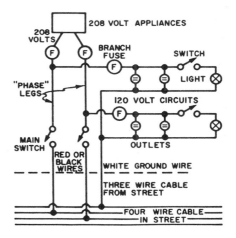

Figure 6: In this system, derived from four-wire, three-phase supply, single-phase power at 120 and 208 volts is available in an average house.

would be in an ordinary three-wire system if each half measured 120 volts; IT IS 208 VOLTS, just as it was in the full four-wire system as detailed previously. Even some professional electricians are fooled; they see three wires and immediately say, "That's 115/230." It takes a voltmeter test and a call to the utility company to convince them the voltages are 120 and 208.

Are there 208-volt appliances? Sure. All you have to do is ask for them. •

ELECTRIC IRONS

You have to take them apart completely to get at the heating element.

These two lightweight travel irons are typical. The one on the left is of the dry type and has a detachable cord. The other has a screw-on water reservoir for steam ironing and a permanent cord.

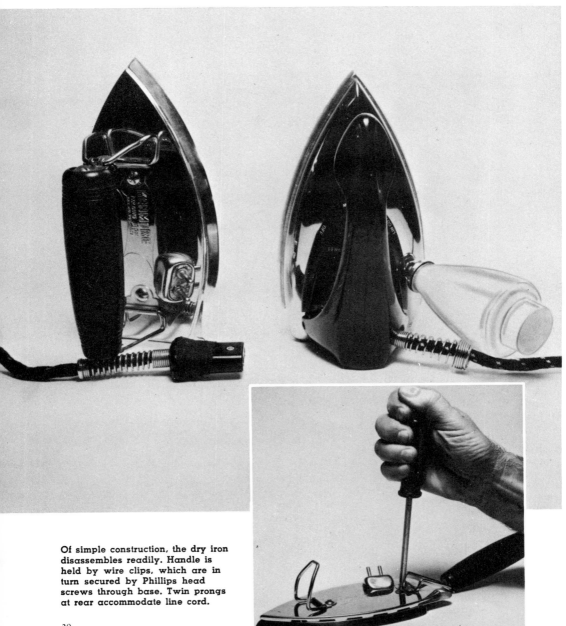

Of simple construction, the dry iron disassembles readily. Handle is held by wire clips, which are in turn secured by Phillips head screws through base. Twin prongs at rear accommodate line cord.

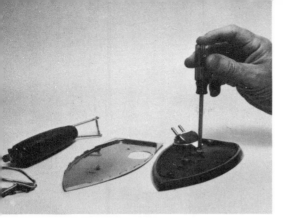

Polished top cover and handle, when removed, reveal a cast iron base. An additional plate here protects the heating element and is held by two more screws. There is no thermostat in this iron.

Heating element consists of flat resistance wire between thin protective sheets of mica. Any possible breaks can be spotted quickly. If element is burned out, a complete replacement is needed.

OF ALL small household appliances, the clothes pressing iron probably sees more service in terms of actual hours than any of the others. It uses a lot of current, runs very hot, is often pushed accidentally off the ironing board and is subject to other forms of mistreatment, so it is bound to need technical attention early in its life.

The line cord particularly takes a beating. Women tend to disconnect it from the wall outlet by jerking at it sharply, a practice that obviously doesn't help it any. In most cases they do this because the plug gets so hot that they are afraid to touch it, and you can't blame 'em. It often pays to install a better outlet, with husky springs to make tight contact with the prongs of the plug. Also, the latter should be bright and shiny.

Almost without exception, the cords supplied with irons, toasters, grills and other heavy current appliances are a special flexible wire, so soft it feels almost like string. The insulation is asbestos, for maximum heat protection. One end of the cord terminates in the line plug and is molded into it in such fashion that it cannot be separated from it. The other end might disappear into the iron and be anchored to screw terminals; or it might be fitted with a detachable flat two-prong plug that fits in a mating outlet on the back or on one side of the appliance.

The latter arrangement offers the advantage of quick and easy replacement if the original cord becomes hopelessly mashed. Replacement cords with fitted plugs are common items in hardware and electrical stores, are inexpensive, and are much less trouble than repairs. As a matter of fact, these special heat-proof cords are a confounded nuisance from the repair standpoint. Once you slice them apart the asbestos tends to fall away, leaving the wires unprotected. The cords achieve their flexibility through the use of many strands of very fine, almost hair-like wire, and it is very difficult to clean them without inadvertently severing bunches of them.

It is easy to check a detachable cord for opens and shorts, as described under the Clicktester, page 18. If the cord is of the permanent type and the iron refuses to heat up, you have no choice but to open the appliance and to look inside for the trouble.

Some irons open readily, others defy all attempts. What often makes the job difficult or downright impossible is the unexpected complication of internal corrosion in steam irons. You remove the handle and the thermostat knob and uncover a big nut or a screw head. These, obviously, call for a wrench or a screwdriver, respectively. You apply the tool and find that it doesn't budge. You lean on it some more; still no action. You squirt a drop or two of penetrating oil to the head and try again, without success.

"It's only a threaded fitting, its gotta give," you mumble. So you take a breath and lean on the wrench or screwdriver with extra oomph. The fitting gives this time . . . maybe. More than likely you find yourself with the head of the bolt or screw in your hand, while the body remains frozen tight. About all you can do now is gather up the pieces of the iron and go out and buy a new one.

Corrosion is especially bad in areas having water unduly rich in minerals. Some appliance manufacturers recommend the use of distilled water to reduce the problem. Study the additional photo sequences through page 37. •

This is representative full-size iron of detachable cord type, with thermostat knob under handle. The first screws in sight are through the handle, so the first disassembly step is to remove them.

Handle "screws" turn out to be one long bolt. The upright brackets are riveted and immovable. Next step is to remove small center screw through the thermostat knob; latter can then be pulled off.

Details of thermostat mounting may not be clear from an examination. With a pair of electrician's pliers pull gingerly on the central shaft, but if it doesn't give right away don't try to force it.

A better approach seems to be at the large hex nut surrounding the thermostat shaft. Use an adjustable jaw wrench, socket wrench or arc-joint pliers, with possible assist from a drop of oil.

 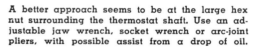 

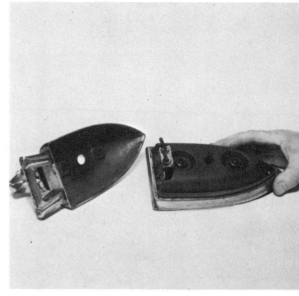

The "nut" turns out to be a deep, hollow threaded stud, whose function is to secure the entire top cover of the iron to the heavy base. Clean the threads with a wire brush or sharpened nail.

The cover now lifts off completely, and two large nuts come into view. The connector for the line cord remains in place, as does the shaft of the thermostat. Nuts appear to hold subbase to base.

Nuts appear to be corroded in place, but a bit of penetrating oil plus lots of leverage on the socket wrench breaks them loose. The iron must be braced to keep from turning as push is applied.

Cast iron subbase now picks off. The threaded studs obviously are anchored in the "sole" of the iron. The line connector and the thermostat shaft are still in place, on another subplate.

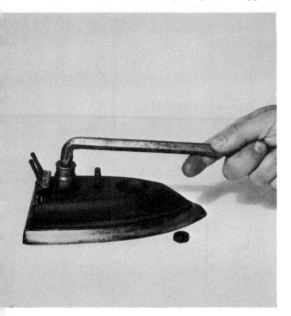

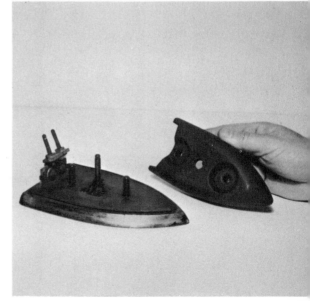

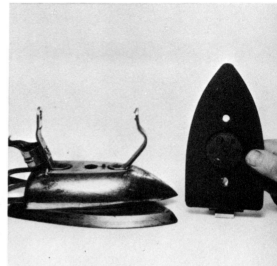

Tugging at the thermostat shaft shows the assembly to be loose of the base. It comes up very easily in one piece. Base is now bare, so heating element must be part of unit just removed.

About the size of half-dollar, the actual thermostat is a black disc set flush in the bottom of the heating assembly. Its purpose is to maintain a uniform heat, to prevent scorching of clothes.

The thermostat is held by two short connecting wires, part of the heat element, secured under screws. Loosen latter and entire thermostat, with control shaft, drops out through a center hole.

With thermostat out, the continuity of the heating element can be checked easily with Clicktester or VOM connected to twin prongs and with the two short tabs temporarily connected together.

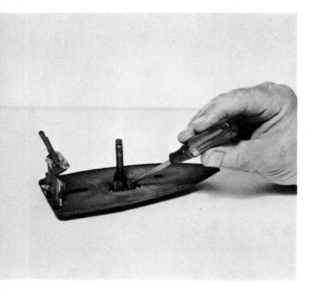

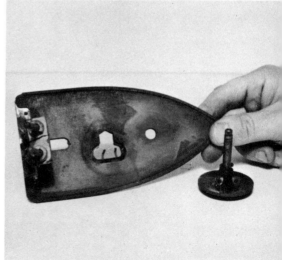

Before halves of heating form can be separated, it is necessary to dismount end prongs. This is a simple nut and bolt job. Observe placement of insulating washers and terminals of heating wires.

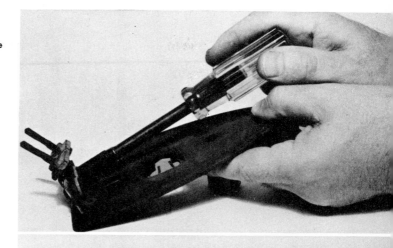

With connector prongs removed, top half of heating element can now be pushed to left, exposing wires inside. Some pieces of mica will come loose. The element consists of flat wire ribbon on mica form.

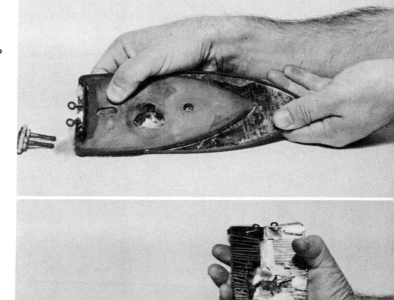

If wire is burned out, install a replacement element. Arrange mica above and below wires to prevent grounding and test with Clicktester to make sure ribbon is not in contact with metal sandwich.

In this iron the cord is attached permanently. It is protected by a spring collar where it enters the body. The thermostat control is a small dial under the back end of the iron's hinged handle.

When the handle is raised a large hexangular nut comes into sight near the front of the iron. This apparently anchors the top cover to the base. The center hole is for water; iron is of steam type.

Well-fitting socket wrench is needed to dislodge the hex fitting. This was badly corroded, and it actually broke off at the last moment. This can be expected to happen with some very old irons.

Even with hex fitting off, cover of iron still was not loose. The only other fastener in sight was the setscrew of the thermostat knob, so this was loosened with aid of small hex setscrew wrench.

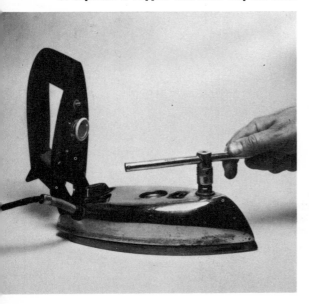

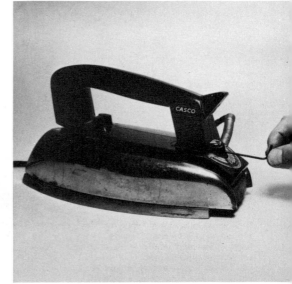

When the thermostat knob was pulled off, another body screw could be seen between the shaft and the handle. This came out readily. Round button next to screwdriver is water compartment seal.

Iron's cover was now loose but not yet removable. Last hitch turned out to be the flexible spring protector of the cord, which unscrewed quickly. Screwdriver points to "snubber" holding the wire.

The cover of the iron now slides off along line cord, and the terminal block for latter becomes accessible. Reason for iron failure is all too simple: one wire had broken away from its screw.

Toaster refuses to get hot, or stays hot, doesn't pop up the way it did before? A quick internal examination may show the fault to be only an open connection, or a large accumulation of baked raisins.

ELECTRIC TOASTERS

Collection of crumbs is usual cause of trouble. A good cleaning helps.

UNLIKE irons, broilers, and similar heat-appliances found in the kitchen, a bread toaster is used only for short periods perhaps once a day. Its wire heating element therefore enjoys a long life and rarely needs to be replaced. "Rarely" does not mean "never." With millions of toasters in active service, hardware and electrical shops find it profitable to stock replacement elements.

Most of the troubles that develop with toasters are mechanical rather than elec-

trical. Crumbs accumulating inside can readily jam up the release mechanism, the control switch, the wire guides that hold the bread in place, etc. If the family is fond of raisin bread, the toaster needs frequent cleaning. Raisins that fall out of the bread are baked by the heat to the hardness of pebbles, and may have to be pried out.

Some toasters have clean-out traps in the bottom. These should be opened once every couple of weeks. Toasters without such traps can merely be turned upside

Old style single-slice toaster has the virtues of simplicity and accessibility. If it stops working every couple of years it can be opened readily for inspection. Four small screws secure the top plate.

Side panels of toaster have small feet which go through slots in base and are twisted here about a quarter turn. Straighten them carefully with electrician's pliers and the panels will come off.

Sides and back of toaster peel off like an orange skin. It isn't necessary to remove front because mechanism connected to push levers is now in sight. The line cord (rear) is permanently attached.

Aluminum pan on bottom of toaster catches crumbs. Remove it frequently and clean it thoroughly with steel wool or abrasive nylon pad. An accumulation here of burned crumbs may give toaster bad odor.

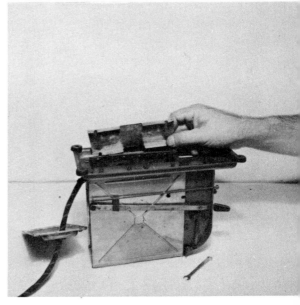

The wire guides that position the bread between the heating elements should fit loosely and come out easily. If they don't, pick them out carefully and scrape them clean with back edge of a knife.

In this toaster two parallel heating elements are held in spring clips in bottom of the base. To remove them, grab top edge with long-nose pliers; give a slight upward jerk to free them from clips.

Breaks in flat ribbon wire of heating element can sometimes be repaired with a patent resistance-wire cement. Joint does not usually last long, so the best bet is to have replacement unit on hand.

It is possible that element doesn't heat up in the toaster but looks good when removed. If continuity checks out with Clicktester or small VOM (below) fault must be in connections to the spring clips.

In this toaster, popping action depends on tension of coiled spring in the bottom plate. This can be adjusted with aid of long-nose pliers. Grab the end of the spring and try it on different notches.

In this more modern toaster, the clean-out plate at the bottom is hinged, and pops open when a button is pressed. Most crumbs can be shaken out, but the stubborn, burned-in ones may need stiff brush.

In a two-slice toaster there are two sets of wire guides to examine and clean. They are easily accessible when clean-out plate is opened. Do not use oil here. Scrape wires, and clean holes with a pin.

Use of screws rather than rivets facilitates opening of this toaster. Here a very small screwdriver takes out a long screw holding color-control knob. Note position of latter's pointer; replace same way.

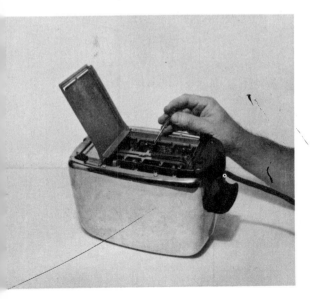

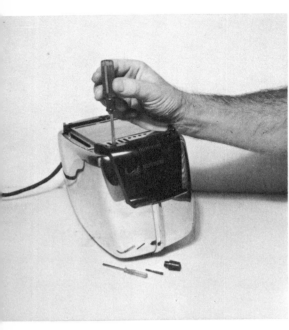

The molded front piece of the toaster, which includes the lever for lowering the bread into the heating chamber, is held by screws at the bottom. Remove slowly; they might be of self-tapping type.

Front of the toaster (below, left) with the molded end piece removed. The small lever that moves the bread holder down is now in view. If it doesn't work freely, it probably should be scraped lightly.

As with other appliances having permanent cords, toaster often develops trouble at point where the wire enters the case. This is aggravated if cord is used by children to pull toaster across table.

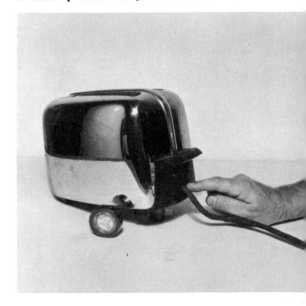

down and shaken vigorously to clean out.

A word of caution here that shouldn't be necessary but usually is: If a piece of bread gets stuck inside a toaster, resist the impulse to reach for a knife or fork and to dig it out. At least, resist for the half-second it takes for you to remove the line plug from the wall outlet. This simple, easy, sensible, obvious precaution can readily save your life. Warn the kids about this.

It just doesn't occur to many people that the red-hot wires in a toaster are very much alive electrically and that silver-plated cutlery is one of the best known conductors of electricity. Because the bread holders of all toasters are quite narrow, it is almost impossible to put a knife or fork into them without making contact with the wires, and then the fireworks begin.

Finally, do not keep a plugged-in toaster on a sink drain or adjacent counter that can become flooded. The water can cause the

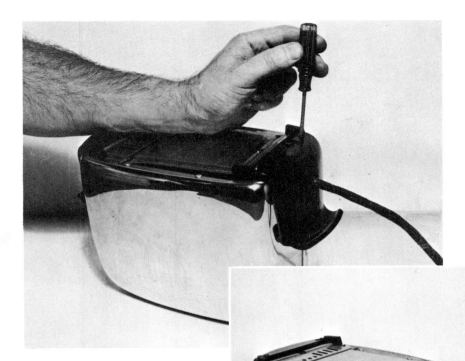

Breaks in insulation close to case cannot be mended unless molded end piece of toaster is removed. Almost identical in shape with front piece, it is held by two screws and can be dismantled in a jiffy.

With end piece slipped out over line cord, insulation and connections are accessible. Cut off loose insulation, then reinforce with a layer or two of tape, pulled tight about an inch each side of hole.

wires to make contact with a resultant surge of power. This is particularly dangerous if you like to bathe the baby in the sink, a common practice. Move the toaster or unplug it.

Sooner or later, it may be necessary to take a toaster apart, at least partially, to release a jammed mechanism, repair the connecting cord, replace the element, etc. Construction varies with make and price, but generally is rather simple. A screw-driver and a pair of pliers are usually the only tools needed for the job.

The accompanying photos show disassembly operations for two toasters: a new two-slicer and a single-slicer 25 years old. The latter is cleaned frequently, has needed only one of its two heating elements replaced in all that time, and continues to make perfectly good toast. The general procedures illustrated in the pictures can be applied to practically all toasters. •

COFFEE MAKERS

Proper use will keep them in working order for years.

Large ten- and eight-cup percolators (left and in center, above) have "strength" controls and pilot lights. Six-cupper (right) has neither and is therefore of simpler construction internally. All make good coffee!

COFFEE makers, like toasters, are used only intermittently, and therefore usually enjoy long life. The way for *you* to enjoy the coffee they produce is to observe a few simple precautions:

1) To assure proper action of the thermostat that controls the heating action, start with cold water.

2) Disconnect the line cord when the pot is empty. Letting it run dry or nearly so can put a strain on the heating element. With liquid to absorb heat from the latter, and with the protection of the thermostat, there is little likelihood of burn-out in normal usage.

3) Don't immerse the entire pot in water to clean it. A few rather expensive makers are so well sealed that they can be immersed, and the manufacturers make a point of this in their advertising. However, by far the majority of pots are not built to take this treatment. As it is, some water is bound to leak into the heating chamber at the bottom. This can cause corrosion in time. It is advisable to open the chamber once in a while and to check for signs of this condition.

4) Don't fuss with the thermostat. This usually consists of a bi-metallic strip that opens or closes as the surrounding temperature changes, and in so doing it opens or closes the power circuit to the heating coil. Because the range of movement is small, thermostats by nature are critical in adjustment. About all you can do with them is make sure that their connections are secure.

5) Most makers have detachable cords.

Six-cup pot looks sealed up tight, but actually only a single large machine screw holds the entire molded plastic bottom to the main body. This makes regular inspection and cleaning quite easy.

Large coiled heating element, center, starts the water gurgling within few seconds after the pot is plugged in. Irregular operation was cured by tightening prongs of receptacle with nut driver.

Bottom of this six-cupper is polished dish, like rest of body. When two screws through it were removed it felt loose, but small knob of thermostat control had to be removed to free it completely.

Bottom dish remains tethered by two heavy wires connecting to receptacle for line cord. Screwdriver points to pilot light, common No. 47 radio item. Flat thermostat assembly is to the right.

The bottom dish can now be picked off to reveal a cluster of small components between two vertical studs. The latter are threaded to take the screws that hold the dish tight against the body.

In this coffee maker the heating coil is entirely enclosed in a solid container, pointed out by finger. The screw that holds bottom dish goes into threaded stud. Parts and wires now accessible.

Large 30-cup party percolator, top, left, has molded plastic bottom, held by one large center screw and four twisted lugs. Note the overhanging spigot. This is vulnerable to damage; treat with care.

After center screw is removed, lugs are twisted straight with flat nose of electrician's pliers. This must be done very slowly to prevent them from cracking off; once gone, they cannot be replaced.

Inspect these in the usual manner for abraded insulation, bent prongs, etc. Incidentally, the same flat two-prong connector that goes into the receptacle on the pot is pretty much standard for irons and grills, too, so in a pinch, you can borrow the cord from one of these appliances.

Some makers include a little red pilot light to tell you that the brewing is finished and that the coffee is ready. This is usually a single-contact, miniature bayonet-base, low-voltage radio pilot, mounted behind a red jewel in the bottom of the pot. Look for a type number on its base, so that you can buy a replacement when needed. The No. 47 is widely used.

Many pots do not have "ready" indicators of any kind. The manufacturers evidently figure that an effective signal, even though it is sort of negative, is the end of the gurgling sound in the glass top.

If a coffee maker really does burn out—it *can* happen—in nine cases out of ten you had better figure on buying an entirely new one. Repair is virtually impossible, or at least both impractical and expensive, because most heating elements are in coiled tubes welded to the inside bottom of the pot. Instead of throwing the appliance away, consider the idea of using it as a flower vase; it might be a conversation piece, if not a particularly noteworthy piece of "pop" decoration.

Some suggestions for getting into several sizes of makers are contained in the accompanying series of illustrations. •

ELECTRIC CLOCKS

They last almost forever, but might sometime need minor attention.

ELECTRIC clocks rarely stop running because they burn out. In most cases the trouble is due to settling or lumping of the lubricant inside. This is bound to happen with a clock that is left fixed in one position for years. A sign of impending difficulty of this kind is a whining noise, like the stripping of gears. This is exactly what it is—the stripping of gears.

As a simple preliminary check, unplug an ailing clock and test it for continuity with the Clicktester or a VOM. The reading on the ohms scale will be several hundred ohms. If there is no reading, check directly at the motor terminals inside.

Some clock motors are not lubricated at all. Once one of these gets noisy or loses time because of gear slippage, the best thing to do is to chuck it away and get a new one. •

First step in checking an electric clock that has stopped is to make sure the cord and the motor are OK. Simply touch the test leads of the Clicktester to the prongs and listen for cracklings.

Similar test can be made with any small VOM. Set it to the X100 resistance range, clip one probe to one prong of line plug, and touch other probe to other prong. Clock should read 300 to 500 ohms.

If VOM gives no reading, indicating open circuit, don't quit. Now remove clock from its case, find the junction of the line cord and the motor terminals, and apply test probes for direct motor check.

No, the picture isn't upside down—the clock is. In nine cases out of ten of motor noise or loss of time, settling of internal lubricant is cause of trouble. Running clock this way resettles it.

ELECTRIC GRILLS

Inspect and check them frequently for "grounding," which can be dangerous.

This is an improved type of grill, with a hinged glass door to confine any spattering. Five-position thermostat is at the left. Permanently attached line cord is out of sight at rear. Sides are plastic.

THE table-top electric "hot plate" was for a long time a popular kitchen appliance with people who either did not have other means of cooking or just wanted to keep their cooking work to a minimum. It consisted essentially of a flat grid of resistance wire in coiled form, about 1/8 inch in diameter, on a ceramic form. Electricity passing through the wire heated it to redness. Pots or pans placed directly over the grid also heated up; not as thoroughly as they would over gas flames, but enough to cook food in them.

The "hot plate" was compact, clean, convenient. There was ("is" is correct for plates still in existence) only one trouble with it; it was frightfully dangerous from the shock standpoint, since the electrically "live" heating coil was in open sight.

Thousands of these plates are still around, many in working order or requiring only minor repairs. Repair may involve only the replacement of the heating coil, a very simple job, but DON'T DO IT. The life you save may very well be your own.

If you find that a hot plate is just what you need for odd jobs around your shop or darkroom, such as melting glue or warming up cold developer, at least take the sting out of it by adding a cover of some kind over the resistance wire. A scrap piece of coarse screening or perforated "hardware cloth" is fine for the purpose. Prop it over the wire about 1/4 inch by means of small stacks of washers or a couple of nuts and secure it with machine screws or self-tapping screws.

The basic hot plate, which generally didn't even have a line switch, has given way to much more elaborate grills having motor-driven spits, thermostatic controls, glass doors, etc. In one style some measure

This squat construction is representative of enclosed type of table-top grill. Heating element is on underside of inside of case. Removable pan holds food. The thermostat is on right side of case.

The line cord is detachable and fits into a receptacle on the back of the case. The flat plug is standard for heat appliances such as toasters, irons. The slots in the case are provided for needed ventilation.

Two necessary tools for disassembly and repair are Phillips screwdriver (left) and a nut driver. With line cord removed, it is safe to put hands and tools inside the grill to loosen fastenings.

Knob of this thermostat has no set screw, but it comes off with a strong pull. On some appliances there may be a set screw through the front of the knob or on side; it might need a tiny hex wrench.

49

Screws come out readily, but the case of this grill was found to be locked together by four rivets through the support brackets of the handles. The heads had to first be ground off, then pushed through.

The manufacturer of this grill obviously didn't want it opened, but with the handle rivets removed it split apart easily. Reassembly later was not a problem, as self-tapping screws did the job of rivets.

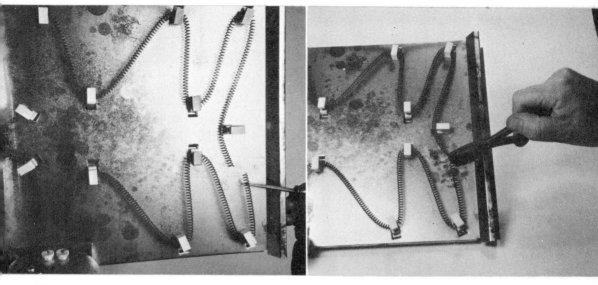

This is what usually puts a grill out of action: the coiled resistance wire has burned or broken open. This can be dangerous to user if the wire touches the frame; it becomes hot electrically.

A temporary repair can be made by twisting the broken ends of the resistance wire together. This might or might not be practical, depending on how brittle wire has become, but it's worth trying.

of protection is afforded by the placement of the open resistance wire *inside* the body of the appliance, at the top or the bottom or both. An oversize pot or pan might still touch the wire, as might a knife pushed in to loosen a burned hamburger, so extreme care is still in order.

The overhead position of the heating element is common because fat dripping from food drops harmlessly to a bottom pan, rather than into the wire itself. However, if the wire should develop a break while the switch is on, and if it drops and touches an aluminum or stainless steel pot, and if the line plug is in the wall outlet the wrong way (wrong from the safety standpoint), and if the cook tries to remove the pot when she realizes the grill is cold—all these if's can add up to one nasty shock.

Under other possible circumstances, a droopy resistance wire touching the pot might put the equivalent of a short-circuit on the line, causing the fuse or circuit breaker on it to open and the whole line to go dead. This is good, if you can call trouble good, because then the entire grill is safe to touch even if the cook forgets to yank the line cord.

All adult members of a family should be instructed to PULL THE LINE PLUG FIRST AND IMMEDIATELY if a loaded grill, or for that matter any electrical appliance, shows signs of malfunctioning. Most people think first of saving the food, but this takes care of itself once the juice is cut off. If the resistance wire should burn out half way through the preparation (as it usually does!) the grill merely goes cold, so there's no real damage. If the thermostat sticks and the grill gets too hot, someone will smell it and rush in, and perhaps save the roast.

Thermostat Control

Grills with thermostat control generally have a single resistance element, distributed inside the case on small ceramic studs. The thermostat does not regulate the strength of the current, as many people seem to think. It keeps it on full until the temperature inside the case approximates its setting; then it shuts it off entirely. The wires cool off gradually, and when the case temperature drops below the setting the 'stat turns the current back on. At the highest setting the 'stat usually keeps the current on steadily.

Simpler grills might have a single three-position switch, reading OFF, MEDIUM, HIGH, or two separate switches marked

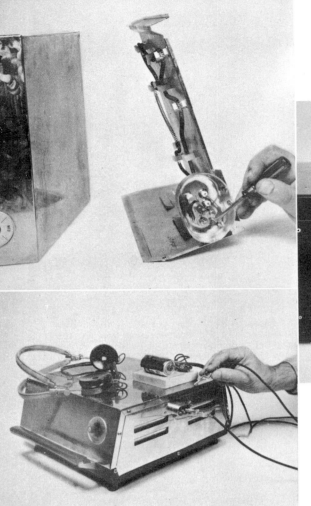

Something that should be done regularly: testing the grill for possible grounding of the internal resistance wire to the case. Turn thermostat to HI to make certain that the circuit is completed.

Either self-tapping sheet metal screws or screws with nuts can be used in refastening handles and sides of grill's case. They can then be removed easily if appliance needs service another time.

MEDIUM and HIGH. There are two separate resistance coils in these appliances; one is brought into play at MEDIUM and both at HIGH. It is entirely possible for a grill to operate at one heat but not the other, since the coils can burn out independently. In a thermostat-controlled unit an open element means no heat regardless of the setting of the control.

One thing can be said for the open-wire type of cooker: the resistance element can be replaced easily, and replacements are available. In fact, it is a good idea to obtain one the next time you're in a supply store and to stash it away with your tools, fuses, spare bulbs, etc., so that you'll be able to make a really quick repair when the original wire gives way.

After installing a new element, check the entire grill for possible "grounds" to the case. The Clicktester or any VOM will tell you positively if the wiring is safe or not. Remember, there should not be any electrical connection between any part of the resistance wire and any part of the case. If the Clicktester makes a noise or the VOM reads on the ohms scale when you touch the test probes to the wire and the body, look very carefully for looseness in the wire.

Protected Heating Elements

The naked resistance element in grills is bound to disappear eventually with the growing use of the slightly more expensive but certainly safer enclosed type. This' is made like an immersion heater; that is, a rigid outer metal casing entirely encloses the actual heating wire, without making electrical contact with it. The heat from the

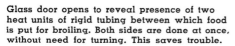

Glass door opens to reveal presence of two heat units of rigid tubing between which food is put for broiling. Both sides are done at once, without need for turning. This saves trouble.

To get at heat units, for inspection and cleaning, it is necessary to unhook front glass door and to pull them a little to the right. They snap out; interior is accessible.

Safety and convenience! The duplicate heat elements are rigid and rugged, are shockproof, can be cleaned with a knife or steel wool, are interchangeable and easily replaced.

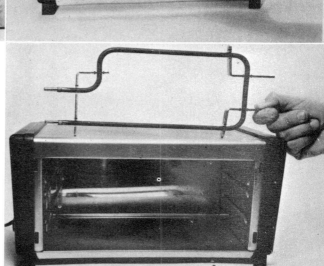

wire is transferred to the casing and the latter gets red hot, but hot or cold there is no danger of shock from it. Food can drip onto the element, but it does no harm and it can be scraped off readily, even with the current on.

A representative grill of modern design uses two such heating elements formed as rigid rectangles partially open at one short side. The ends of the elements are fitted with plugs which fit neatly and quickly into tight jacks inside the body of the appliance. Pull them out, and the smooth, unbroken) surface of the grill can be cleaned in a minute. A burned-out unit can be removed and replaced by a new one in less time than it takes to read this sentence, and without tools of any kind!

Grills are in the same heavy-current category as irons, toasters, space heaters, etc. Their line plugs must be clean and fit tightly in the wall outlets. The cords must be protected from abrasion; and if they are of the detachable type, from getting lost.

General Maintenance

Examine the insides frequently, taking particular note of the condition and position of the heating wires if they are of the exposed variety. Try not to drop or jar the appliance, as this can cause the ceramic insulators holding the wires to crack or break off. When replacing plug-in heating elements, brighten the end connectors with fine sandpaper, emery cloth or steel wool and push them back firmly.

After cleaning the whole grill dry it well and make sure it is still dry when it is used the next time. •

SPACE HEATERS

Enjoy the comforts they offer, but treat them with care and caution.

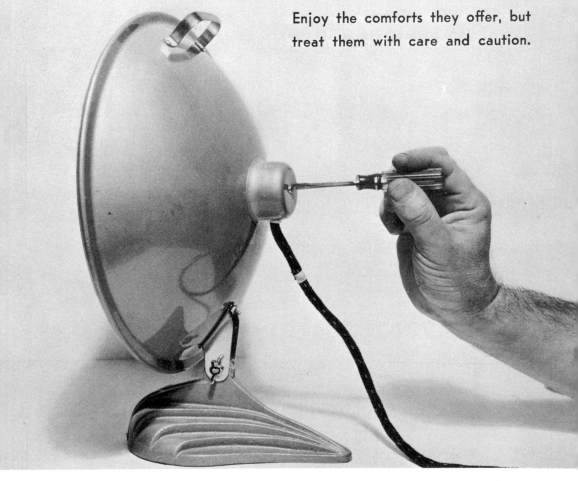

Representative bowl heater is hinged to a heavy base. Heater unit is in cup at back of reflector; removal of screw makes it accessible. There is no switch. Heater is controlled by the line plug only.

GREAT for taking the chill out of a room at the end of the line of a house heating system, portable space heaters are also great consumers of electricity. The bowl type takes 500 or 600 watts; larger models with self-contained circulating fans up to 1650 watts, the safe (and legal) limit on 110-120 volt circuits. In areas where electric energy is cheap and 220-240 wiring is available throughout a house, heaters taking 3000, 4000 and 5600 watts are common.

Small heaters consist usually of a coil of heating wire at the focal point of a polished metal shell. You simply plug 'em into an outlet and they're on. Larger ones have switch-selected degrees of heat intensity or fully automatic thermostat control; also, cutoff devices that turn off the current if a heater is upset accidentally.

Some inexpensive bowl-type heaters are potentially rather dangerous because their removable protective grills are of coarse mesh through which fingers, knifes, sticks and other objects can be poked quite easily. The possibility of burn or shock can be reduced if an additional covering of ½-inch square "wire cloth" is fastened over the factory-installed grill. This material is open enough to pass the radiated heat.

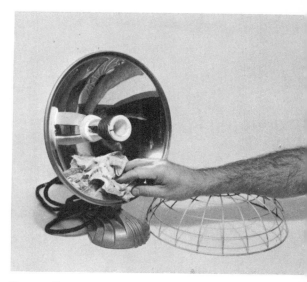

Heating element consists of coil of coiled wire on ceramic form. Line cord connects directly to screw terminals at base. Replacement coils are readily available. Simply wind in place, connect.

Heater effectiveness depends mostly on a shiny reflector. Unplug line cord, remove protective grill and clean frequently with soft cloth. The open grill should have a closer mesh for safety.

Spring-loaded plunger on bottom of the fan-operated heavy-duty heater mystifies many owners. It is an "upset" safety switch. If the heater is pushed over it cuts off current regardless of main switch.

Ordinary window screening, which has spacing of only about $\frac{1}{16}$ inch, is a bit fine for the purpose, although it will serve in an emergency until the ½-inch mesh can be obtained. Some types of sheet grillwork is also suitable. This is thin aluminum, punched out in a variety of designs and patterns. It is often used as a decorative cover for room radiators.

Still on the subject of safety: The bathroom has long been known as the most dangerous part of the house, because of falls in the tub or shower. Don't make its record worse by putting an open space heater near either of the latter. It is all too easy for a person with a dripping hand or foot to establish a circuit between the room's plumbing, which is very thoroughly "grounded," and an electrically "hot" part of the heating element. It's better to chatter a little while getting dry than to risk electrocution.

Tight connections and clean plugs are essential to safe heater operation. The heating effect at points where there is appreciable resistance is aggravated by the fact that the power loss here is a function of the *square* of the current. To take some round figures as an easy example, suppose

a dirty plug has a resistance of one ohm and the appliance takes four amperes. The simple formula for electrical power in watts is the current squared times the resistance. In this case the answer is merely four squared, or 16, times one, or 16 watts. Suppose a larger appliance requiring eight amperes is used. The heat loss is now eight

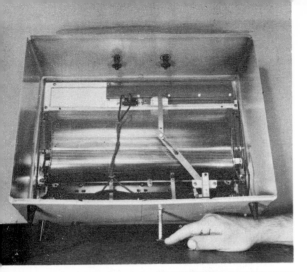

This is same view as in previous photo, but with the back of the heater body removed to show the back of the straight reflector and the internal wiring. Arm near center is control of thermostat.

squared, or 64, times one, or 64 watts!

Because plugs depend on mere sliding friction to make electrical contact with the brass fingers inside wall outlets, some slight resistance here and hence some heating effect must be expected. If you put your hand on a plug and feel only mild warmth, the contact is adequate. If it it too hot to hold, you need an outlet with tighter springs to bite into the prongs of the plug. It's easy enough to clean the latter, but there's no way of getting into the outlet.

The efficiency of electric heaters depends largely on the cleanliness of the reflecting surfaces, whether they are bowl-shaped or flat. The heat attracts dust, so frequent dusting is important. A very slightly dampened rag does the trick.

The elements of all electric heaters turn red and can quickly ignite paper and cloth. The appliances should therefore be used with great caution if small children are likely to be within reach of them. Kids are naturally inquisitive and find the warm glow irresistible.

If the cord furnished with a heater is too short to reach the nearest available outlet, use as least No. 16 or preferably No. 14 asbestos insulated flexible wire for the extension. Also, cut off or unscrew the present line plug and make soldered joints where the old and the new cords meet; then add the plug to the end of the extension. Most factory-installed cords have molded plugs that cannot be opened or used a second time. Discard them after they have been removed.

When buying a new plug look for one with a heavy base, preferably reinforced by a metal ring, and with husky screw terminals that can take No. 16 or No. 14 wire. Avoid the dime-store plugs of "molded mud." They just aren't made to carry 15 amperes for any length of time without starting to melt. •

Blower fan is on inside of back cover of heater. It is being checked here for continuity after it stopped working. Nothing was really wrong; one of its wires had merely shaken loose from terminal.

A smart safety check: with switch on, heater is being tested for possible "grounds" between the line cord and the body. "Grounding" does not affect heat, but makes body potentially dangerous.

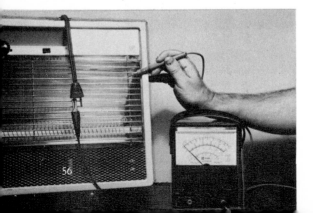

56

To repeat, space heaters can be warm friends, but they can also be hot-headed enemies if you are not careful with them. Generally, keep them out of the bathroom—and away from small children.

The time to become acquainted with your fuse box is when the electrical system of the house is in normal order. Make a record of which fuses control which circuits and keep the spares near the box.

FUSES ARE FOR SAFETY

Keep assortment of spares on hand for those emergencies.

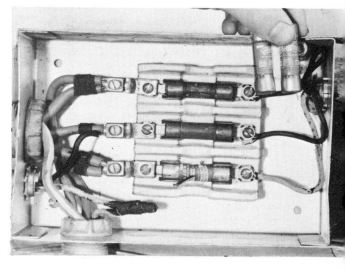

Cartridge type fuses are generally used on heavy current circuits such as those feeding electric ranges, central air conditioners, etc. Contacts exposed; use wooden stick to pry.

FUSES and circuit breakers are the safety valves of the house electrical system. A fuse burns out or a breaker snaps open, like a switch, when the current rating of the device is exceeded by an accidental short-circuit on the line or when too many heavy-current appliances are plugged into it at the same time.

In most homes the individual branch circuits from the meter use No. 14 wire and are intended to carry 15 amperes *safely*. If a fuse or breaker of this size opens frequently, there simply are too many appliances in use; they should be distributed among two or more branch circuits. Putting in larger fuses is sheer insanity. This can only lead to wiring fires.

More and more builders are putting circuit breakers rather than fuses into new homes because these devices cannot be corrupted. Fuses can be screwed in and out in a moment, but breakers are installed on a permanent basis. If one snaps open, you can reset it by pushing handle back, but you can't change its current rating.

Clothes washers take a rather heavy current for a few seconds on starting, and then a much lighter current for running. Circuits feeding them should be fitted with special fuses called "slow-blow," which are designed for this tricky operating action.

Fuses are cheap. Keep a handful in a handy place, *along with a flashlight*. Trouble is much more likely to happen at night than during the day, because that's when everybody is home and using lamps, TV, radio, etc. •

REFRIGERATOR

Though infrequently used, these can break

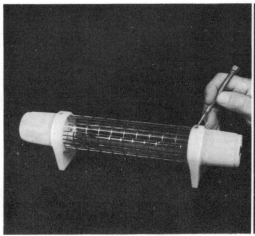

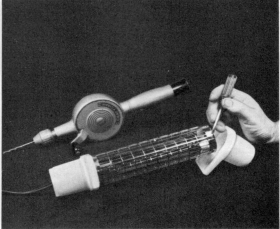

This type of defroster has a metal cage for its body and plastic end feet. The latter are fastened by blind rivets, put in with a special tool. Cord emerges from one foot. There is no switch.

If defroster appears to be defective and element needs to be tested, the only way to get into the cage is to drill out the rivets. They are generally hollow and collapse completely when drilled.

BECAUSE of the normal moisture in the meats and fruits kept in a refrigerator, ice is bound to form in the freezer compartment. Over a period of several months the accumulation can be large enough to crowd out packages of frozen food that should fit comfortably. "Defrosting" then is imperative.

To many housewives this is a nuisance job because they must first empty the compartment, wrap the food to delay softening, and then fill the space with successive pots of hot water. The pot routine is quite ridiculous, because for a few dollars you can buy a "defroster" that does the melting quickly and painlessly. This is nothing more than a small electric heater, very much like a section of a toaster or grill. The heating element is enclosed, so it is not affected by melting ice dripping onto it. The food still has to be removed, but the rest of the work is done by the defroster.

The system is to place the device inside the freezer compartment, to close the latter's door carefully over the line cord without bruising it, and to do the same with the refrigerator's main door. Leave the defroster on for about fifteen minutes

Of all metal construction, this style of defroster resembles a small griddle. An insulated handle makes it easy to hold when it heats up. Melting ice falls safely through top and bottom openings.

and then examine the ice for signs of softening. Usually you can hasten the defrosting by poking gently into the ice with a stiff knife; it will fall off in chunks, which can be swept out readily.

Since it is needed only a few times a year, a defroster should last almost in-

DEFROSTERS

from handling and storing. Here's how to make them right.

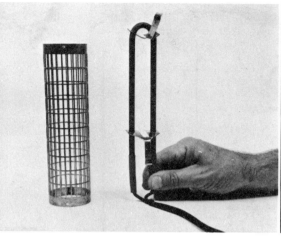

Disassembly effort may not be worth while, since actual heater wire may be enclosed in metal tubing and not accessible. However, faulty operation may be due only to loose conections at end.

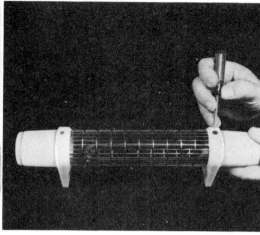

If repair consists only of tightening loose connection, reassemble the cage and feet with small self-tapping screws or even short 4/36 or 6/32 machine screws. These will bite into the plastic.

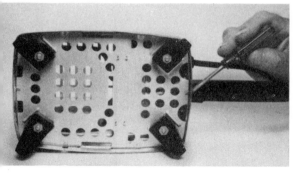

The bottom plate is held to body of defroster by twisted tabs. To remove plate for internal inspection, straighten the tabs slowly with flat-nose pliers so that they line up with slots in body.

definitely. It should, but it doesn't always. It usually suffers damage from being kicked around from one storage spot to another. In many households the cry is, "Where did we put the darn thing?"

Pay particular attention to the line cord, and especially don't slam the refrigerator doors hard against it. The wires inside the insulation can sometimes break even though the insulation doesn't. An indication of this trouble is an intermittent sound when the Clicktester is used or a jumpy meter needle when a resistance check is made with a VOM.

If a defroster fails to heat up, the heating element possibly is burned out or more probably there is something wrong only with the line cord. The only way to get at the truth of the matter is to open the device, if it can be opened at all without wrecking it. Screws yield to screwdrivers, but blind rivets usually have to be drilled out and then replaced by hardened self-tapping screws. If the heating element really checks out as open, it is usually cheaper to buy a whole new defroster than to waste time looking for a replacement element. If the line cord is OK, remove it and save it in your junk box. It's bound to be useful for future repair purposes.

In buying another defroster, look for one with a metal rather than a plastic case. Some of the imported plastics, known as "molded mud" in the trade, don't hold up very well to the extremes of heat and cold to which they are subjected. •

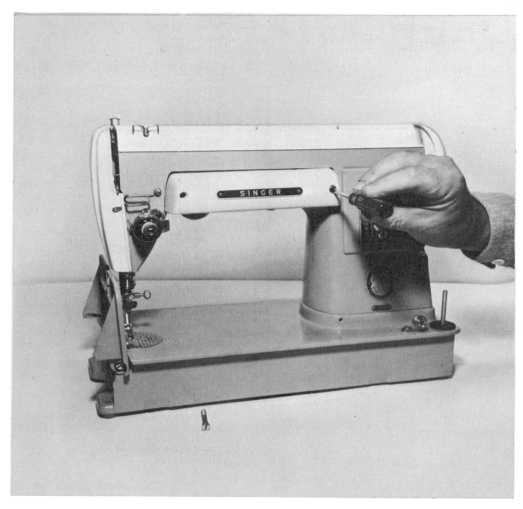

More modern style of sewing machine, with motor concealed in base, above. Electric light in reflector over work surface may require replacement often because of vibration. Cover screws remove easily.

ELECTRIC SEWING MACHINES

A small variable-speed motor makes needlework an easy job.

PROBABLY the first important power operated device in American homes was the sewing machine. Only a small motor was needed to replace the foot treadle, and it made the machine infinitely easier and more pleasurable to use. Nowadays treadle models are considered antiques, and often bring higher prices than they did when they were new.

There are two general types of electric sewers. In one, the motor is out in the open behind the hand wheel that sets the starting position of the needle. A small rubber disc on the end of the motor shaft bears against the rim of the wheel and drives it by simple friction.

Mounted behind the main head, the motor of older sewing machine is out of the way of the user but is completely accessible. Finger points to one of two brushes, easy to get at in insulated sleeves.

Mounted on a spring-loaded bracket which pushes it against the large hand wheel, the motor turns the latter by means of a small rubber roller on its shaft. Keep these surfaces clean, free of oil.

Inspect motor drive frequently, check for tightness of pulley, and oil motor bearings sparingly. Good idea to have spare pulley on hand. Clean the contacts of large plug, check cords for abrasion.

Speed control of machine in previous pictures is of stepped type. Screwdriver points to strips of resistance wire stretched between eyelets in insulated base. These warm up in normal operation.

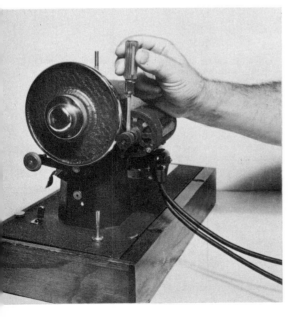

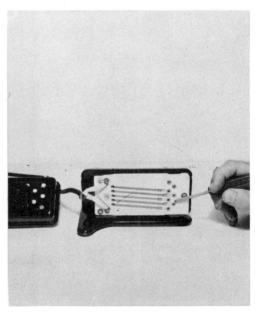

Because of space limitations, lamp is usually a small one with bayonet base of type found on auto bulbs. Magnifier glass in reflector concentrates illumination on work being fed into needle area.

There are two power cords for this machine. The one from speed treadle (left) plugs into receptacle at bottom; the line cord plugs in under the wheel. Plugs are different designs, can't be interchanged.

Foot Speed Control

The motor speed and hence the sewing rate are controlled by a small foot treadle. This actually is a "rheostat," the common electrical term applied to a variable resistor. With no pressure on its foot plate the power circuit to the motor is open. As the treadle is depressed the internal mov-

Interior of speed control (top, left) is rather simple. Main item to inspect is the spring that actuates the foot pedal. This is likely to move out of position. Also check out all screws for tightness.

For protection (above) against bits of cloth and thread, "works" of machine are usually well covered. In this model the bottom plate is held by a single large thumb screw through the center.

The drive motor is mounted vertically in a corner of cast base. Latter is ribbed for rigidity. A plastic cover protects the motor against dust. It comes off easily when two visible screws are removed.

ing contact touches one end of the resistance wire, closing the circuit and causing the motor to turn over slowly. Further pressure moves the contact along the wire to a lower resistance setting. This increases the voltage to the motor, so it speeds up. With the treadle all the way down the machine is at maximum speed.

Anyone who drives a car learns to use this control in a minute, as it duplicates exactly the action of the accelerator.

There are several types of rheostats, some using a compressible carbon pile instead of wire, but the voltage regulating effect is the same.

In the second style of sewing machine

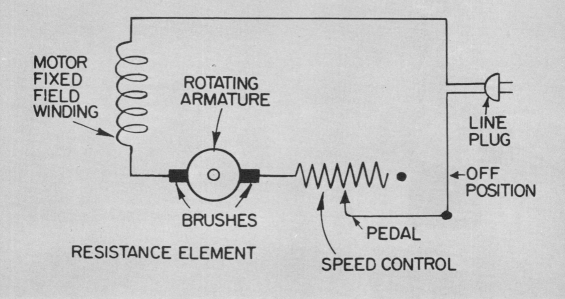

MOTOR
FIXED
FIELD
WINDING

ROTATING
ARMATURE

LINE
PLUG

←OFF
POSITION

BRUSHES

PEDAL

RESISTANCE ELEMENT

SPEED CONTROL

Basic wiring diagram of motor section of a typical sewing machine. The speed control might be of the continuously variable or step-adjustable type.

Carbon brushes are in square brass sleeves near the end of the shaft. If they spark excessively they should be replaced. Trick in removing them is to take the tension off the retaining springs.

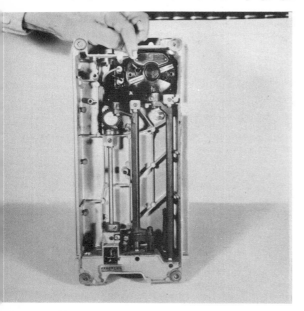

the motor is concealed in the base and drives the needle mechanism through gears and shafts. This is the arrangement found in most modern machines because it lends itself to attractive, streamlined designs. The speed control is the same as before.

Almost universally, the AC line cord and the wires from the foot pedal connect to the back or side of the machine by detachable plugs. When the machine is not in use the cords can be wound around the pedal and the package stowed in the carrying case. Virtually all sewers these days are "portable" in the sense that they can be encased and then stored in a closet.

The motor is rated about 1/12 horsepower, on the average, and is of the "universal" type. This means that it has two small brushes, which will eventually need replacement. Other maintenance is purely mechanical; mostly, it consists of applying small quantities of thin oil to bearings.

The speed control is what needs particular attention because when in use it is constantly jabbed and released; literally, it takes a beating. Check frequently for loose screws and connections and for damage to the connecting cord. A good precautionary measure is to put a couple of layers of black electrical tape over the cord for a distance of about a foot away from the treadle.

The accompanying pictures show representative models of the two styles of machines mentioned herein. •

WORTH KNOWING

Here are some hints that may prove useful in your repair of appliances.

Handy Test Light

TEST LIGHT (at right) is useful for determining if circuits are dead or alive. Wire guard is from photolamp; socket is the brass shell type, bulb of any wattage. Wires are soldered to nails taped to wooden dowels.

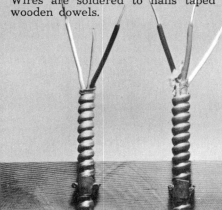

Types of Wire

SOME of the types of wire found in homes (left to right, above) are the two-wire "BX" with bare ground wire; three-wire BX; the two-wire "loom" with bare ground wire; three-wire loom; individual insulated wires usually encased in a thin-wall steel conduit. Usual sizes are No. 14 & No. 12. All wires solid copper.

Safety Extension Cord

ONE OF THE handiest items you will find in shop or garage is a good, long extension cord, at least 25 feet, using three-wire cable, three-prong safety plug and receptacle. Connect the wire with black insulation to the brass colored screws, and the green to the green screw. •

ELECTRIC BLANKETS

They're great on cold nights if you keep them dry and in good order.

ELECTRIC blankets and their smaller versions known as "heating pads" differ from other heat appliances such as toasters and irons in that they need much less current. They are always used quite close to the body, so the paramount consideration is safety.

Here is where maintenance is more important than repair. The fact to remember about both blankets and pads is that their heat is produced by thin wires sewn between two layers of cotton, wool or other material. Externally, electric blankets look like any other kind, but because of the wires they must be handled with special care. Pads are less critical only because there's less of them to handle.

Do not throw a blanket into a shapeless heap on the floor or a chair while making a bed, and do not stuff it tightly into a drawer. As much as possible, keep it flat, or at least store it loosely if it is not left on the bed during the day.

By all means save the original box in which the blanket was packed, and use this for summer storage. Follow the lines of the factory folds and the whole cover will then fit the container comfortably.

Cleaning an electric blanket isn't as difficult as it might sound. In the better grades the heating wires are strong and flexible enough to withstand agitation and tumbling in an ordinary home washing machine. Some models can't take this treatment. Play safe by following the manufacturer's recommendations, without deviation.

One answer to the cleaning problem is to minimize it by keeping the blanket clean. Always use a cotton top sheet between the blanket and the bed, and change and wash this frequently to prevent build-up of perspiration and body odors. If the blanket is well aired every morning it may not require actual laundering more than once a year, at the end of the winter season. Consider how often or rather how infrequently an ordinary blanket is cleaned, and then put the electric model on the same timetable.

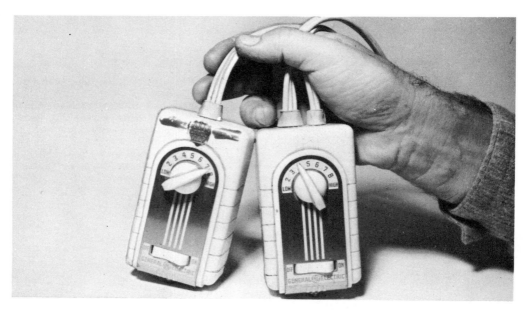

Pair of typical "his" and "her" thermostats for control of two separate electric blankets or for the individual halves of a large double blanket. On-off switches are at bottom. Knobs set the temperature.

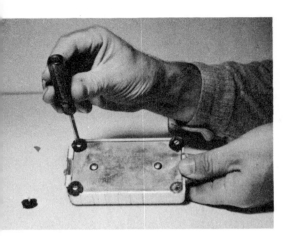

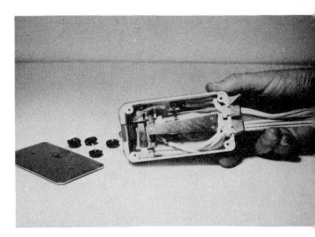

Plastic cases of thermostats have metal bottoms, in this model held by small screws through soft rubber feet in corners. Removal by means of suitable Phillips screwdriver takes only few minutes.

Become familiar with inside of control unit when it is in working order, and then you'll be able to recognize possible points of breakdown. Interior of unit is simple but adjustments are critical.

This control unit for a single electric blanket looks like a small radio set. There didn't seem to be any way of removing knob until closer examination revealed that dial button was removable.

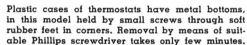

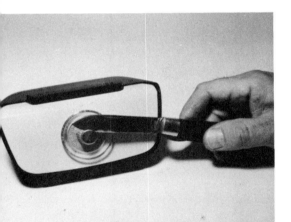

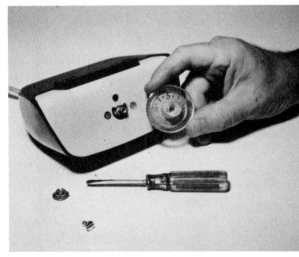

With the dial off, two screws that were previously hidden by it came into view. The hole directly above the shaft permits light from a small lamp inside the case to illuminate the dial's figures.

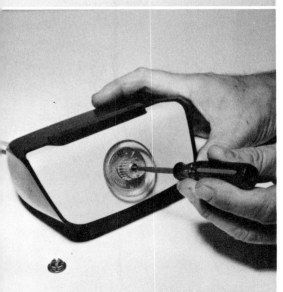

After the button was pried off with knife blade, small screw was found in the center of the heat control shaft. This was removed easily, and then the dial could be pulled off the splined shaft.

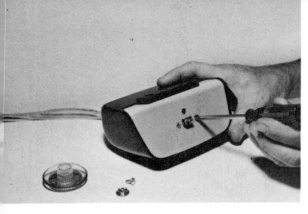

The two screws fasten the decorative front panel of the control unit to a sub-panel. When these were taken out the front panel came off completely. To avoid loss, keep the screws in small box.

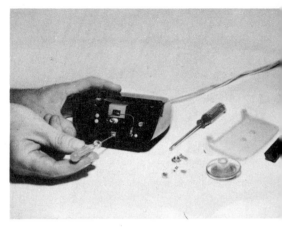

Final disassembly was now completed with removal of one small screw in front panel. Chassis moves out in one piece, grommet, cable follow.

Further disassembly, at left, was delayed because there was no sign of additional screws through the bottom. However, a little poking indicated rubber cable grommet might be involved.

It definitely was. It was very tight, but when its top edge was pushed down with a screwdriver it moved inward and immediately gave the inner chassis a loose feeling. Grommet protects wires.

With eight wires in the cable entering the control unit, it pays to make sure that all connections are secure. If leads are color-coded, make a sketch of their placement, for later reference.

More or less standard type of heating pad is similar in internal construction to the electric blanket, but has two-way heat control instead of variable thermostat. The switch comes apart for checking.

People who suffer from incontinence should be especially careful about using electric blankets, or perhaps they shouldn't use them at all. Not to be indelicate about it, but the fact must be faced that human urine is decidedly acid chemically and a good conductor of electricity. A wet electric blanket certainly poses the possibility of danger.

Heat Control Important

It's easy enough to pass electricity through wires and to make them hot; the trick with electric blankets is to keep the temperature from going too high or dropping off too fast. This control is provided by very sensitive thermal sensors in conjunction with heat-adjusting boxes designed to sit inconspicuously on a night table.

An electric blanket takes a little getting used to. After the first five minutes it feels too hot, so you turn down the control a notch or two. Then it stays cool too long before it comes on again, so you turn the control up. This can go on all night unless you strike a compromise that lets you sleep.

A couple sharing a double bed and one large blanket can have a real problem, because women have a thicker layer of outer tissue than do men and can withstand cold better. A thermostat setting that keeps him warm will have her kicking the blanket off within minutes, and then neither will be happy. Several alternatives are available:

1) Get a blanket with a split heating element, each half controlled by its own thermostat.

2) Use two entirely separate blankets, each with its thermostat.

3) Switch to twin beds and separate blankets.

4) Move to Florida.

Because the current required by a blanket is relatively small (the wires get hot, but they never reach the glowing stage), the element lasts almost indefinitely if not abused, and the thermostat likewise is dependable. Dependable, that is, until a disturbed sleeper winds himself up in the blanket and pulls the entire little control box off the table. If the floor is carpeted it might bounce a bit but continue to work. If the fall is a hard one it might not. The least you can do then is to open it and see if you can spot any fixable damage, such as a loosened wire, a cracked case, etc. The cases are generally molded of plastic, and can often be patched with cellulose cement or any kind of sticky tape.

Heating Pads

About the size of a hand towel, heating pads are intended for localized applications of heat, particularly to treat sore muscles. They do not generally have thermostatic control, but do have low and high switch settings. About the only thing likely to go wrong is the switch itself, because it is snapped on and off a great deal in normal service and its light internal contacts have a tendency to break off. Its two halves are held by screws and can be opened easily for inspection. The two-wire line cord enters at one end, and a three-wire cable emerges from the other and goes to the pad proper. The three wires are part of the heat-control circuit.

Treat a heating pad as you would an electric blanket: keep it clean and dry and refold it neatly after each use. •

69

ELECTRIC FOOD BLENDERS

They're working properly if they make lots of noise. How to keep them noisy.

Waring blender, an invention of popular orchestra leader, has a heavy base containing drive motor. Rotary switch gives choice of low or high speed. The mixing bowl is readily removable for cleaning.

To check for possible "grounding" of case, a dangerous condition, turn on speed switch, connect VOM in turn from case to prongs of line plug. No reading means that internal insulation is intact.

Make note of internal resistance when appliance is in normal order. Typical readings on blender are zero ohms with switch off; about 30 ohms with switch at low speed setting; and 8 ohms in high.

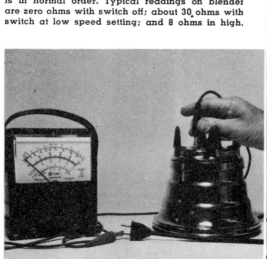

IN ITS MOST widely used form, the electric blender consists of a small motor that drives a set of metal blades in the bottom of a detachable glass vessel. Screaming around at high speed, the blades can whip up almost any combination of liquids in seconds and can reduce many pulpy fruits and vegetables to thick liquids in less than a minute.

The most vulnerable part of a blender is the glass jar, on two counts. First, it is rather top-heavy and can be knocked over readily. Second, it has a hole in its base through which passes the short axle of the mixing element. When the jar is set over the base of the blender, which contains the motor, this axle engages in a mating hole in the latter's shaft.

Like the propeller shaft assembly of a boat, the opening in the glass must be tight enough to keep liquid from leaking out but loose enough to allow the blades to turn without binding. With average use the packing material at this point should last for several years; with a lot of use the life will obviously be shorter. Removing old packing and installing new is largely a matter of having wrenches of the right size and reach. If the glass jar is nicked from repeated falls, it is sometimes less trouble to buy a new one, complete with blade assembly.

Some blenders have only one speed, high; others have high and low settings, selected by a three-position switch. The third, of course, is "off." Sometimes the machine will groan and refuse to run when the switch is turned from off to low, but will start in high and then run in low when the switch is turned to that setting. This is an indication that the jar is overloaded with too much solid food or that the axle is binding in its packing. The latter is certainly the case if the difficulty occurs with the jar empty.

Erratic motor operation may be due to dirty or bent switch contacts. To get at switch, look for set screw in knob and loosen. If no screw is visible, pull knob straight off, with tool assist.

With this particular blender, knob turns out to have an extension stud, all molded in one piece. Body of switch is mounted to the case of the appliance by a knurled nut, which must be removed.

To prevent marring polished case of the blender, use pliers with thin jaws to loosen the nut of the switch. At this stage of experimenting with appliance, removal of bottom plate is necessary.

of short screws, or held by pull-out clips to which connecting wires are pinched or soldered. Because brush-type motors are generally favored for machines requiring high speed, such as mixers, blenders, vacuum cleaners, etc., replacement brushes are stocked by most hardware and electrical supply stores. It's nice to get exact replacements for a particular appliance, but it's also very easy to adapt larger brushes merely by dressing them down on sandpaper or emery cloth.

With bottom plate removed, the switch can now be pulled out and examined. One case of spotty motor operation was cured by application of hot soldering iron to joints between wires and terminals.

Sensibly fitted with screws to facilitate cleaning and inspection, blender's bottom plate comes off easily. Three screws pass through rubber feet. Note if food has splattered here, and sponge off.

Motor brushes, which may need replacement at some time, are held in metal guides near end of shaft. In this blender, they are released when connector clips leading to guides are pulled out gently.

If the operation of the machine is satisfactory otherwise, don't monkey with the packing, as this can be difficult to get at in some models. It takes only an instant to twiddle the switch from one position to the other.

The motor is generally quite well protected in the base of the blender, but because it undoubtedly uses brushes it should be examined once a year or so. The brushes are actually two little bars of carbon in spring-loaded holders mounted diametrically opposite each other. They bear against the "commutator," a ring of copper strips to which the windings of the rotating part of the motor are connected. Some sparking between the brushes and the commutator is normal, as is brush wear due merely to friction against the relatively harder copper.

The functioning of the brush-commutator assembly can be observed closely if the cover of the machine is removed. The brushes might be secured under the heads

When a clip is removed the brush with its spring attached pops out of its holder. Somewhat soft, carbon does wear down. Brushes should be replaced when they get down to about ⅜ inch.

To prevent its ends from pulling away from connections inside blender, cord is snagged to bottom plate by a small clamp. This is held by screw, removable if cord ever needs replacement.

Excessive oiling is a common cause of trouble in motor-operated appliances that are run only for short periods. A small drop of household oil, once in 6 months, is enough for this blender.

Blenders are run only for short periods and therefore can get by with very little lubrication, or none at all. If there is a hole in the baseplate directly over the bottom end of the motor shaft, resist the temptation to squirt oil into it. Don't even squeeze the can; just let *one* drop leak out of the spout into the opening. Excess oil can readily find its way to the commutator, and since oil is a very good insulator it can literally gum up operation of the motor.

The usual caution against submerging appliances in water to clean them applies to blenders. Any liquid that slops over from the jar can be wiped up readily with a damp sponge. •

FOOD
MIXERS

They are easy to keep
running with a little
attention to lubrication.

Standard pedestal style of food
mixer. Speed control is directly
under user's thumb, near handle.
Motor mount is hinged, so that
entire head can be tilted back for
mixing blades to clear the bowl.

THE FAMILIAR style of food mixer
consists of a heavy cast base, a platform
for a bowl, and a motor head on a pedestal.
In most models the head can be detached
and used free-hand in any loose bowl, but
generally it is a bit heavy for this purpose.
The lighter and more streamlined hand-
held type is favored by housewives and
amateur male chefs for whipping up everything from eggs to souffles.

The labor-saving element in all mixers
is a small, high-speed motor of the AC-DC
"universal" design. The fact that it can
work on DC as well as AC is of little im-
portance because DC has disappeared
from probably 99.9% of all American
homes. However, the expression "AC-DC"
seems to appeal to advertising copy writers
and it appears in many pieces of sales
literature.

A variety of mixing blades can be fitted
quickly by means of snap-in chucks, which
are on short shafts at right angles to the
main horizontal line of the motor. Some
blades are made of rather soft metal and
are easily damaged if the mixer is put
down on a work surface before the motor
comes to a complete stop. To prevent this

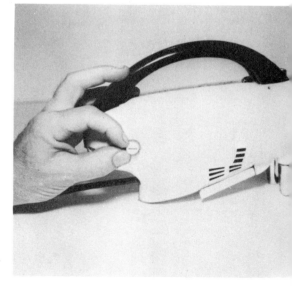

The motor assembly slides easily off the top of
the pedestal mount, and stands comfortably on its
front twin chucks. The brushes of the motor are
at rear end of case. Their caps unscrew quickly.

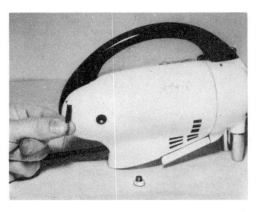

The small brush is of standard carbon type, with a fine wire spring attached. This keeps the end of the brush in firm contact with the "commutator" on the rear end of the motor shaft. Read down.

With the end off you can see that the grease in the gear box has settled well below the two gears connected to the twin chucks, leaving the drive mechanism dry. Shaft is lubricated, gears aren't.

In this mixer, small holes are provided in front and back of housing for lubrication of the shaft. Don't squirt in oil; too much can foul the commutator. Let in one, solitary drop in each hole.

Redistribute the grease thoroughly, putting more of it near the top than at the bottom. This will keep the gears lubricated for another long period before it settles to the bottom of the case again.

Does the front end of the mixer sound grinding, noisy, even after addition of oil? This calls for opening the appliance and making sure that gears aren't stripped, or shaft bent, or just plain dry.

Light weight mixer can be used comfortably with one hand. It has no stand of its own, but when it must be stopped for a moment it can be rested on its heel, just like an iron. Speed control at top.

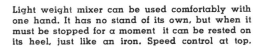

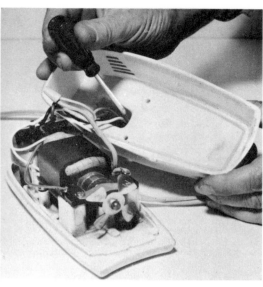

With the mixing blade removed, the portable mixer sits flat on the table, can be mistaken for an iron! Entire body top comes off when 2 screws are removed. The slots are for motor ventilation.

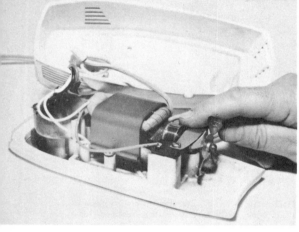

Completely in the clear when the top of the body is folded back, the motor and the gear assembly are easy to examine and clean. Finger points to copper commutator, against which brushes press.

Speed control switch is in handle, cannot be inspected readily. With single mounting screw removed, it drops out. In foreground, at end of the motor shaft, note small fan, for forced cooling.

damage, as well as the annoyance of spattering food all over the kitchen, get into the habit of leaving the blades in the bowl and waiting for the motor to stop after you turn off the switch. This sounds like a rather obvious suggestion, but many people can benefit from it.

Check the Brushes

Maintenance and repair of a mixer is largely a matter of checking the brushes, applying a bit of lubricant to the bearings (but only if the manufacturer's instruction sheet calls for it), and keeping the entire machine clean. In most models the brushes are readily accessible, being held under flat, slotted screws that require only a dime rather than a screwdriver.

One sign of impending brush trouble is

intermittent sparking and sputtering, accompanied by a strong odor; actually, that of ozone. Also, there might be grinding noises in a nearby radio receiver or broken-up pictures in a television set.

By the very nature of its applications a mixture is sure to inhale some of the froth it stirs up. An accumulation of this stuff inside the case can in time certainly affect the operation of the motor, so periodic cleaning is advisable.

If not kept clear of the work area, the cord of a hand-held mixer can sometimes get entangled in the whirling blades, with results that are more often funny than serious. If the user can't get at the switch fast enough the bowl might spill, pudding might decorate the walls, and the cord might acquire a few bruises. The small

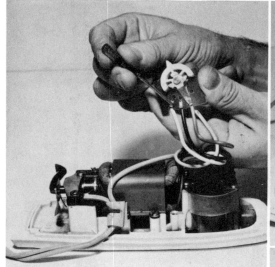

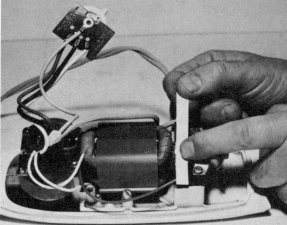

Examine contact surfaces of speed control switch for encrusted food, and scrape clean with small screwdriver or knife blade. Also pull lightly on connections to be sure there are no cold joints.

Motor will run smoothly and without sparking if the commutator is kept shiny. Hold a narrow strip of fine sandpaper against it with one finger, and turn rotor slowly by means of fan at end of shaft.

Check all mounting screws for tight fit. Look for a set screw in stud of small ventilating fan and secure it well. Before reassembly of body of mixer blow out or scrape away all food incrustations.

motor doesn't usually develop enough energy to sever the wire. A layer or two of electrical tape or white adhesive tape should take care of the bruises.

Lubrication of Gears

In all mixers, the right-angle drive mechanism uses gears of some kind. These might or might not be "lubricated for life" at the factory. If the appliance seems to get noisier and noisier with use, possibly the grease has leaked off gradually, or, more likely, has simply been thrown away from the gear teeth by centrifugal force. Fortunately, most mixers come apart easily, and a quick inspection will indicate whether more grease is needed or if the grease already there merely needs to be spread around better.

Speed control is an essential element in mixers, as the requirements of various preparations are different. The pedestal style appliance usually has a wide range of adjustment from very slow to very fast; the hand-held type, at least medium and fast. If the motor runs well at some settings of the control but poorly or not at all at others, the switch contacts are probably encrusted with batter of some kind. Usually, just scratching them clean with a small screwdriver is all they need. Actual breaks in connections are also to be expected, because of the normal vibration of the appliance.

In the accompanying picture sequence two mixers are shown in various stages of disassembly. The job is quite simple and requires only a screwdriver. •

FANS

The most effective place for them is in the attic of a house.

To see if it would really do any good in a hot attic, a large belt-driven fan was mounted temporarily in this manner against an opening in a dormer. It shook a little, but cooled the attic!

Improvement in house comfort was so noticeable that the fan was put on firmer support (top, left) and front edges were taped where they met siding. This eliminated leakage, gave even better draft.

Outer view of installation, above, before it was prettied up. Roof overhang protects against rain, screening against birds and insects. Louvers are better, but more costly. Pole is for TV aerial.

Another good installation of an attic ventilator. Powerful 24-inch fan is enclosed in plywood box, which can be opened for inspection and lubrication of motor. Louvers can be seen through blades.

FOR COOLING

LET'S START with a disclaimer: *fans do not cool*. In some circumstances the heat of their motors might actually raise the temperature instead of reducing it. But fans move air, and air moving through a moist area promotes evaporation, and evaporation tends to cool the immediate vicinity. Since it is high humidity rather than heat that makes people uncomfortable, it is safe to say that fans at least make us feel better.

Sitting in the direct blast of even a small fan is unhealthy. A fan is most effective if it is mounted in a window and can exhaust air from the room or rooms to the outside. There has to be air coming in from another opening to maintain the flow. This can be a window of another room of an apartment, or, best of all, a basement window.

A fan is particularly effective in removing the blanket of stagnant air that is always found in an unventilated attic during the summer. If not disturbed, this is what makes the upper bedrooms of a small house feel like ovens. The bigger the fan the better; for an average five- or six-room house, not smaller than 24 inches in diameter, and larger if it can be gotten in. The technique is to mount this in front of an opening in the side of the house and to leave the attic door or access trap open, so that fresher air from below will push out the stale attic air.

The difference in house comfort produced by this system of forced ventilation has to be experienced to be believed. People coming in from the outside on a summer day, when the temperature is close to 90, will invariably exclaim, "This air-conditioning is really great." It isn't the kind of air-conditioning they think it is, but it's still noticeable. •

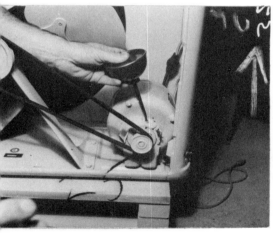

In hot weather the attic fan might be kept running for days on end, so lubrication of motor is important. Look for oil filler caps at both ends.

Bearings of belt-driven fan usually take grease rather than oil. Apply sparingly and often rather than heavily and rarely. Excess grease tends to work out and is spattered around by the fan.

With every lubrication job, check tightness of fan, motor and fan pulleys, belt, motor mounting bolts, and electrical connections. Running all day and night is bound to put some strain on 'em.

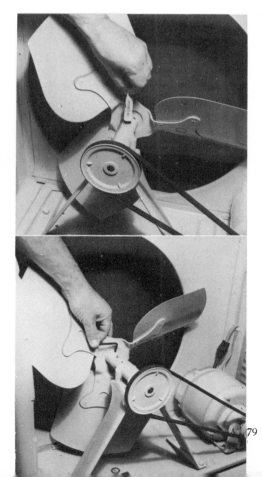

ELECTRIC CAN OPENERS

Does a neat job safely and quickly and leaves the can reusable.

Electric can openers have a characteristic look: A vertical shape, two small angled cutting wheels and pivoted arm to secure the can. Small model at the left can be used on table or hung from wall.

CONSIDERING the number of cans of various kinds found in the American home, it is no wonder that the electric can opener is rapidly becoming one of the most popular labor-saving devices in the kitchen. It ranks high as a gift for newly-weds because it is not only useful but inexpensive.

An electric opener consists essentially of a small, high-speed motor connected to a pair of cutting wheels through a high-ratio reduction gear, usually of the worm type. The cutters develop considerable torque and easily bite their way through the rim of ordinary cans. In doing so they leave smooth edges, which means that the empty cans can be reused for many purposes.

Because this appliance is run for only seconds at a time it can be expected to give long service. Most models are "lifetime" lubricated; some might need a dab or two of light grease on the reduction gear every few years.

If an opener seems to be unduly noisy, perhaps the internal lubricant has settled to the bottom of the case and is not being distributed properly to the gears. As a cure

An opener in working condition does a fast, easy job on cans and simplifies meal preparation for housewife and bachelor alike. Magnet just above cutters holds the lid after it has been severed.

Finger points to major trouble spot in can opener: the junction of the two cutting wheels. Food accumulates here, hardens, and often interferes with operation. The area should be kept clean.

First step in cleaning representative opener is to remove magnet that holds lid after cutting is finished. This usually just pulls straight off, or in some models it might be held by two screws.

Upper cutter is not powered by the motor, but revolves with can as lower cutter turns latter. It is usually held by a hinged tooth, which can be released by a scratch awl or a small screwdriver.

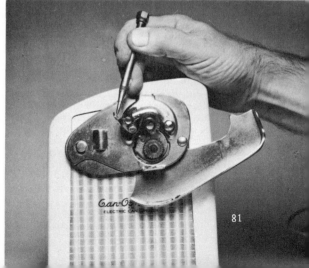

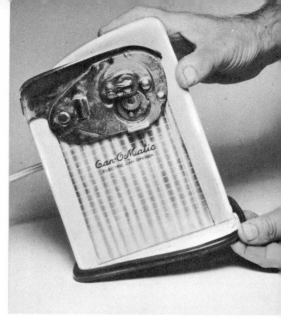

Since cutters dig into a can and touch its contents, food is bound to stick to them. Scrape removable cutter with a knife, and clean out the teeth of the powered wheel with a pointed tool.

Want to see what makes a can opener work? Disassembly is generally easy, once you find where body screws are located. They weren't in sight on this model until the bumper on base was removed.

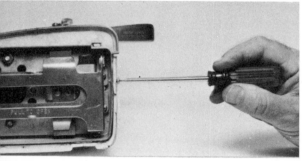

Case of opener is held to base by short screws of self-tapping type. Remove them carefully with well-fitting screwdriver to avoid mashing threads.

Case slides only this far because the line cord apparently is snagged short inside the case by a pinching-type plastic insulator near the bottom.

try the old clock trick of inverting the appliance. You can't very well run it this way, but if it is kept in a warm spot, like a radiator or the top of a gas stove that has a pilot light, the grease will certainly drip down to the gear train. This may not work with all styles of openers, but it is certainly worth trying.

What does require periodic attention is

the exposed cutting mechanism. When a can is being opened, some of the contents is bound to stick to the cutters or to drip over to the magnet that grabs the can's top. If enough of this goo hardens on the metal surfaces it can interfere with the operation of the device. First try brushing with a soapy solution. If this doesn't leave the area clean and bright, scrape with the

Vertically mounted motor, right, is seen to have worm gear on shaft that drives a larger gear at a much reduced rate. The motor switch is in small box, next to shaft. Its cover is being removed.

The trick in loosening the line cord insulator is to squeeze the narrow center part against the rim and at the same time to pull forward. It then slides out of hole along cord; case is now free.

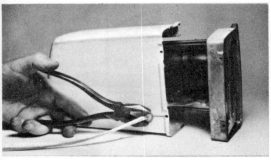

Of single pole momentary contact type, the motor switch has two leads to its terminals. Its snap opening and closing under tension of spring can be observed as opener handle is pushed, released.

Clicktester connected to the prongs of line plug gives loud response if motor and switch of opener are intact and handle is pressed and released several times. No sound is indication of trouble.

blade of a very thin screwdriver or the point of an old knife, and brush again.

The motor of an opener goes on when the handle that clamps the can in place is swung to its closed position. The actual switch is inside the case. Like all switches, it can sometimes stay either open or closed.

The switches in can openers are all of the momentary-contact type. That is, they close to "on" only as long as the clamp handle is kept down to hold the rim of a can. Remember this when checking a switch for its ability to close and open a circuit, either with the Clicktester or a VOM.

One of the openers shown in the pictures stopped working after it had been used only

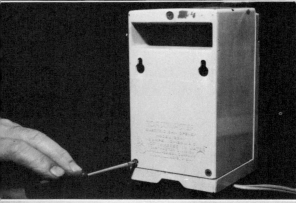

In this can opener, left, above, the upper cutting wheel and the handle are part of a single assembly, which is held by two thumb screws. These can be taken out in a few moments, for inspection.

Handle assembly removed, above, powered wheel is now in the open. The gear-like teeth around its rim are best cleaned with a scratch awl. If this is not available, a large pin will serve.

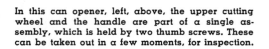

No trouble finding the screws on this can opener! There are two short ones along bottom edge and one long one at the top. Slotted holes above center line of case are for hanging unit on wall.

Reduction drive in this model consists of double pair of gears, with the motor in the normal horizontal position. A slight application of lubricant (auto grease, Vaseline, etc.) quiets the gears.

a few weeks. A check with the Clicktester hooked to the line plug indicated an open circuit. It seemed unlikely that the motor would go bad so soon, so the appliance was disassembled. When the very last two screws, on the switch housing, were removed, the cause of the failure was immediately obvious; one of the switch wires had worked itself loose. A three-second application of a hot soldering iron fixed it. •

DOOR BELLS

All they need to keep ringing are clean door buttons and some AC.

HOW many times have you visited people to find a sign taped to the front door, "Bell out of order. Please knock"?? Actually, it is very rarely that the bell itself is "out of order." It is operated for a few seconds at a time only a few times each day, and therefore should last forever.

In nine cases out of ten the bell doesn't ring because the bell button outside the door has dirty or corroded contacts. This is not surprising, since it is exposed to all kinds of weather. It is overlooked only because it is such an insignificant little object.

A bell button is held by two screws, which are easily removed, and it has two connections, which are also easily removed. If you touch the bare ends of these wires together and the bell clangs immediately, you know that a new button is all you have to buy. Usually it doesn't pay

to spend the time to open the old one.

In the tenth case the bell ringing transformer that you'll find near the electric meter or the fuse box probably has a loose connection or two. How these develop is a bit mysterious. Most likely, the repeated slamming of a nearby garage door or the rumbling of passing trucks is responsible. Anyway, merely tightening the binding posts often gives the bell back its voice. It isn't necessary to turn off the juice; the voltage here is only about 14 or 16.

The exposed brass binding posts of this transformer represent one of two windings called the "secondary." The other winding, the "primary," is connected permanently to the AC line, usually by short wires disappearing into the fuse box. Most transformers of this type feel slightly warm; this is normal, and no cause for alarm. •

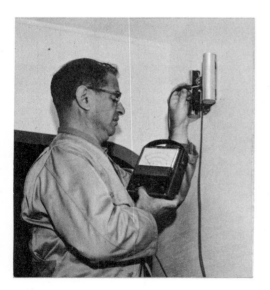

Is low-voltage AC from the transformer reaching the bell? To find out, jam a toothpick into the bell button, set the VOM for low-range AC volts, and touch test prods to binding posts of bell.

The button outside the door is most likely cause of bell failure. When removing it for inspection and probably replacement, pull out wires carefully. They are usually solid and break easily.

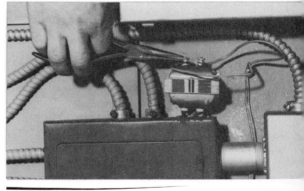

Erratic operation of a door bell can be fault of loose connections at the small transformer near the fuse box. First undo them, scrape them clean with knife, and refasten them well with pliers.

85

VACUUM CLEANERS

The long cords are vulnerable, but their big motors are easy to work on.

The vacuum cleaner probably takes the worst beating of any household appliance because it is used frequently, is dragged around mercilessly by its own cord, and is expected to ingest dust, buttons, string, pins, paper clips, etc., without developing indigestion. It also uses the largest motor, up to ½ horsepower.

In all models, fan blades of some kind are attached directly to the shaft of the motor. They are shaped and directed in such a manner that they draw outside air through the cleaning nozzle and its flexible hose and into the dirt collecting chamber, a detachable cotton sack or a disposable paper bag. Strictly speaking, the expression *"vacuum* cleaner" is a misnomer. The system isn't really air-tight enough for a real vacuum to develop. It is probably more correct to say that the intake of air at the opening of the nozzle lowers the atmospheric pressure in the immediate vicinity of the latter. The other air in the room is heavier and rushes in instantly to fill the space. Any moderately light object that happens to be in the way is whooshed into the appliance.

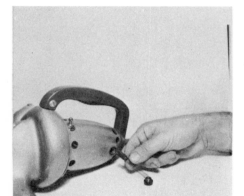

In small hand-held vacuum cleaner, usually used for furniture, brushes are at end of case and are easily removed for inspeciton or replacement. The switch is under handle. Holes are for ventilation.

It Blows Out Too

If the air pressure at the nozzle is negative, in the sense that it is lower than that of the room air, it is very much positive at the other end of the system. Advantage is taken of this situation in many cleaners to provide a powerful blast of air which is particularly useful for operating accessory sprayers. The air by itself is great for dislodging dust, insects, etc., from places that cannot be reached with a regular nozzle. The blower fitting, normally closed by a little trap door, takes the same flexible hose used for vacuuming.

Cleaner motors are of the brush type and therefore require the usual inspection of the brushes themselves. In small hand-held machines the latter are accessible from the outside. In most larger machines the motor is usually enclosed in the case. Accessibility is generally good, because the cases have to open easily anyway for cleaning or replacement of the dirt sack.

A vacuum cleaner does cleaning, but

One reason why this cleaner sounded odd: tangle of string and dirt was caught in blades, could not free itself. Fortunately, entire motor and blower assembly is held by only 4 machine screws.

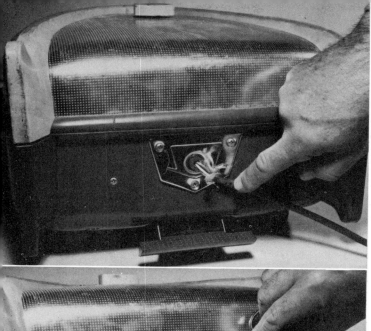

Heavy cleaner was dragged around by its cord; result, outer insulation at point of entrance into case wore away. A little more of this mistreatment and cord would have short-circuited to case.

Wires themselves were intact, so all loose insulation was trimmed away with scissors and thick layer of electrician's tape was wound as close to case as possible. Pedal is on-off foot switch.

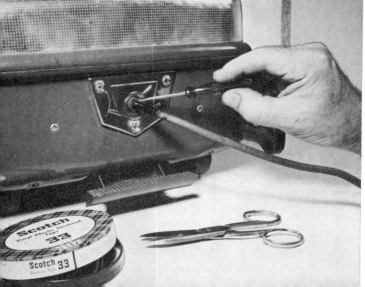

Soft grommet in case permitted taped cord to be pushed in with thin screwdriver. This is important; otherwise tape doesn't really protect wires. Often the repair is easier if grommet is removed.

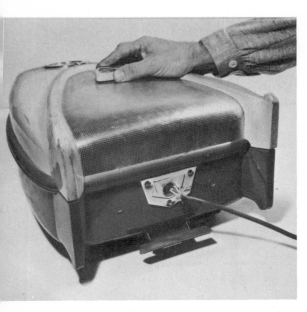

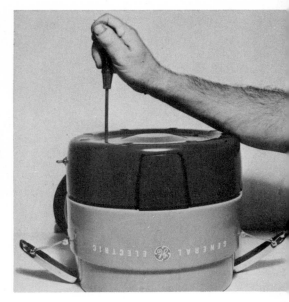

Access to inside of this flat-type vacuum is from top. Decorative knob in center is actually lock. A quarter turn in either direction, top comes off. The cord can be wound around rear "ears" of case.

The first step in inspecting a vacuum cleaner is to open it up. In this typical canister machine the first screws in sight are six through the bottom. Remove screws carefully; avoid stripping.

Motor operation was irregular. Switch was prime suspect, so it had to be removed. Connections to line cord and motor here are by twist-on caps, which are loosened by pliers or by the fingers.

If connections do not yield readliy, don't waste time fighting them. It's usually easier to snip them off with side cutters and to resolder them later. The folding clamp secures top of cleaner.

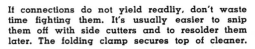

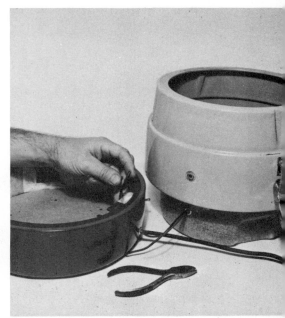

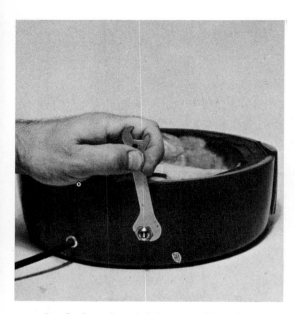

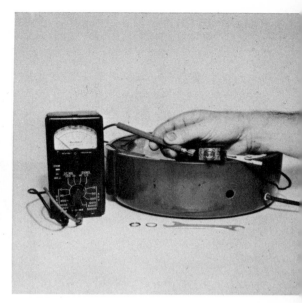

Standard toggle switch is mounted by a large hex nut on a threaded stud. Remove it with a wrench, not pliers. Latter will almost always damage the finish. This "pan" is the bottom of the cleaner.

On-off switch is removed from case for convenience in testing with small VOM. set to read LO OHMS. Jiggling of needle with the switch on indicates bad contacts and need for replacement.

Motor appeared to be mounted in sieve-like cage in bottom of top half of the cleaner. Six more screws around mounting rim could be seen. Some were already loose, probably from motor shake.

Perforated cage lifts out readily and is followed by the motor, which is mounted in an upright position in a shallow metal dish. This area has to be cleaned occasionally; perhaps once a year.

With motor removed from case, top, left, the brushes and the commutator are in view. Here, one of the brush retaining strips is being removed, so that the brush can now be examined for condition.

Spring attached to brush, above, keeps it in firm contact with copper segments of the commutator. Note size of brushes and obtain replacements. Commutator's black from carbon, needs a cleaning.

To restore brightness of commutator, rub gently with small strips of fine sandpaper, NOT emery cloth. Clean s u r f a c e s reduce sparking and carbon wear and minimize radio & TV interference.

itself it needs occasional cleaning. Unless a second machine is available in the home, this is best done outdoors with a long-handled brush that can reach into all corners. Check the direction of the wind and keep on the safe side. The fine dust that comes out can be very irritating.

If a cleaner gradually loses some of its early sucking power and a new dirt bag doesn't help, look into the flexible hose. Very frequently this is partially blocked by knots of carpet fuzz and string snared against trapped pins or toothpicks. A little poking with a rifle cleaning rod, a plumbing "snake," or some similar long, round object, usually dislodges the obstruction.

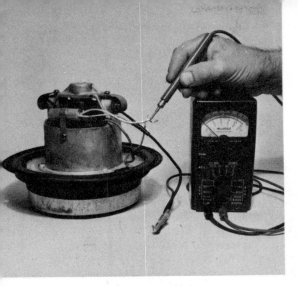

Commutator sparking and hence radio/TV interference are further controlled by "suppressor" unit on motor frame. This is actually a small capacitor. With motor exposed, check it with VOM.

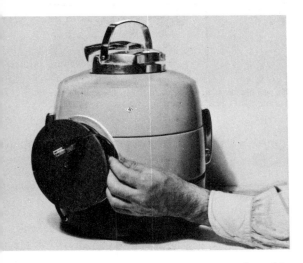

Home-made reel for vacuum cleaner cord consists of two discs of hardboard with center separator. It is mounted loosely to case with one machine screw so that it turns easily. Slot holds plug.

Air leakage in the hose is due merely to cracks. You can locate these easily by running your hand along it. Electrician's tape is fine for patching them, since it's flexible.

The Cord Is Convenient

It's no use telling a woman (or any other user of a vacuum cleaner) not to pull the machine along the floor by its cord, and not to disconnect the line plug by yanking at it. Sometimes the nozzle is a good tow line, but the cord is much longer and is easier to hold. So face it: you must examine the wire often, over its entire length for abrasions and other damage to the insulation, and at its ends for actual breaks. Line plugs of the molded type are quite strong and can take a lot of punishment, but there's a limit. The really weak point is where the cord enters the case of the machine. There is usually a grommet or other kind of ring here. A soft grommet cushions the flexing of the wire, but a metal one merely grinds its way into the insulation. When the latter becomes frayed, it is usually fairly easy to open the case, disconnect the leads, cut off three or four inches of the cord, form new leads, and connect them. If the grommet is big enough, reinforce the cord at the point of entry with tape. Most cords are 15 to 20 feet long, and the loss of a few inches isn't noticeable.

The on-off switch of most vacuum cleaners is foot operated and even the most rugged ones loosen or bend in time. In some models it is only a small toggle switch, but it can be kicked up and down with the toe of a shoe. This type was never intended for kicking and it doesn't last long.

Some cleaners of well-known make have absolutely no provision for storing the long cord. When a machine is put away in a closet the wire is usually left in a heap on the floor, where it is stepped on and otherwise mistreated. As minimum protection, form the wire into a loop about a foot in diameter, flatten it down about half way, and secure the loose ends with a couple of thick rubber bands. It can then be hooked over the handle of the cleaner, or held between the body and a wall.

Probably because they are buried inside the cases of the machines, most vacuum cleaner motors are designed not to require lubrication by the users. Their bearings are usually oversize and may have enough factory-filled grease to last a long time. In general they give very good service; they rarely fail completely. The usual incidental items are what need attention: brushes, switches, cords.

The accompanying picture sequences show three entirely different kinds of cleaners and what might have to be done to them. •

Next stop, the junk yard. Everything valuable or usable has been stripped from this worn-out washing machine, as it should be. The motor was still in good shape and is now running a powerful attic fan.

SALVAGING PARTS

Before discarding that worn-out appliance, search it for useful hardware.

DRIVE on a Monday morning through almost any suburban community in the United States and you'll be struck by an odd sight: here and there, sitting unhappily at the curb, is a partially dismantled clothes washer, or perhaps a dish washer, or an air conditioner, or a mangle . . . down the line to a sprinkling of grills and toasters. It may not be true that appliances, like automobiles, have obsolescence built into them at the factory, but it sure looks that way.

The clothes washer is the commonest discard, probably for the reason that it does more real physical work than any other household device. In a family containing several children the parents are lucky if a washer survives the period from the advent of the first one to the arrival of the second. There are *always* diapers to do!

No Trade-In Value

The trade-in value of used appliances is virtually zero. If you shop around for a new one a dealer will offer you what looks like a generous allowance for your tired washer, and then he'll tell you to junk it. He won't even bother to take it away, unless he has a connection with a local scrap metal yard. He doesn't lose any money by his "generous allowance," because most list prices are highly inflated and are only the starting point for bargaining.

It is a pity just to put an appliance on

the street and wait for the sanitation people to pick it up. (And even that takes a special appointment in some cities!) Even a machine that has stopped working altogether is not valueless. Stripped down to the last removable component, it can yield a rich treasure of useful odds and ends.

Consider the usual clothes washer. Cut off the line cord and you have a fine replacement for use with any electrical device. Trace the internal wiring until the motor is free, and then dismount it. It is usually a ⅓ horsepower unit of rugged construction, ideal for the operation of a grinder, a buffing wheel, a jig saw, a medium-size bench saw, a water pump, an air compressor, an attic fan, a garage door opener, etc. Yet people unthinkingly let it disappear with the garbage!

Motor Can Be OK

Although the motor is the heart of a washer, it does not "go bad" nearly as much as owners believe. Many are equipped with thermal cutouts that open the AC line in case of a severe overload (that is, too much dirty laundry); others simply blow the line fuse if they stall. Much more common are failures of the water control valves; of the clutch mechanisms for fill, agitate, drain and spin; and of the timer that controls these actions. The motor can still be in perfect running condition after all these devices have expired.

The mere mounting hardware in the average clothes or dish washer is worth several dollars if you buy it new. Sturdy bolts and nuts as large as ½ inch, lock washers, springs, brackets, clamps, etc., all will surely be valuable for the repairs that always have to be done around a house.

The timer is nothing more than a geared down clock motor. Remove the cams that actuate the exposed switch levers and you have the basis for a variety of small toys to amuse youngsters.

Of simpler construction than a clothes washer, a dish washer still yields a rich harvest: again a motor, perhaps a little smaller than ⅓ h.p.; a timer; hardware; and often a beautiful propeller of brass or hard plastic. The function of the latter is, of course, to splash the water around the dishes, which are stationary. If nothing else, it makes an odd decoration, a conversation piece, in a den.

"Oh, that?" you'll probably say to guests. "From my wrecked dish washer." They were probably expecting you to say "from my wrecked yacht," so they're bound to laugh.

Air conditioners and refrigerators are not usually good pickings because much of their mechanism is sealed. Of all household appliances they enjoy the longest life. One of the earliest refrigerators was the General Electric "monitor top" introduced in the 1920's; thousands of them are still making ice cubes more than forty years later.

Remove Refrigerator Door!

If you must discard a really "gone" box, do not fail to remove the door before you put it out in the cold. You'll sleep better knowing that no child will suffocate to death after locking himself in any refrigerator that *you* once owned.

Small appliances can be just as rewarding as large ones. Many a hair dryer, vacuum cleaner, food mixer, etc., ends up at the curb only because of some trivial fault: a broken brush in a somewhat inaccessible motor, easily replaced if the latter is dismounted; a heating wire grounded to the case, giving off sparks and frightening the owner out of keeping a dryer; a grease-jammed timer in a table-top grill, preventing the spit from turning; and so on. You can fix the troubles and restore the machines to normal operation; or, if they are too dirty and scarred, you can at least strip 'em for parts. Give boys a couple of wrenches and screwdrivers, and they'll keep busy for hours at this work.

Small Hardware Is Useful

Don't overlook small items such as headless set screws with slotted or hexagonal female ends; ⅜ and ½ inch hex nuts used on the mounting studs of toggle switches; soldering lugs and terminals; shafts, pulleys and bushings; gears and cams; all pieces of insulated flexible wire more than about a foot long; line plugs and similar friction-type connectors; small lamps and pilot lights; fuses, circuit breakers and thermal overload protectors; insulating washers; brackets and clamps; leveling feet; etc. Keep these odds and ends in labeled cigar boxes, and you'll find yourself dipping into them frequently.

Some things like thermostats are not worth salvaging because they are designed to work under specific conditions in particular appliances and are not likely to work satisfactorily in others. But do take off screws, nuts, washers, etc. •

ELECTRIC KNIVES

These are simple motor-operated devices that are easy to keep in order.

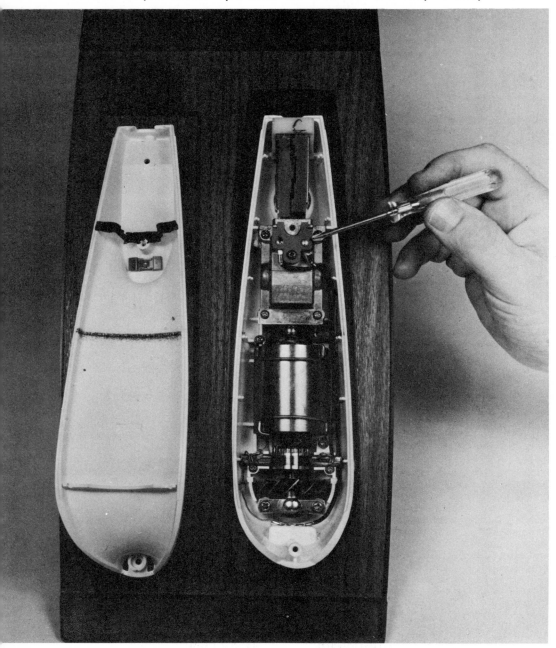

Opened lengthwise like a pickle, the electric knife is seen to have very neat, simple and accessible "works." Screwdriver points to contacts of the switch. Blades fit at top. Drive motor is at the bottom.

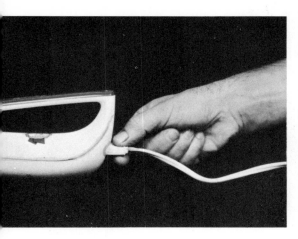

DO. When inserting or removing the line plug of knife, push or pull with a firm, straight motion. DON'T. Don't grab cord and pull or twist. In time this will surely damage both cord and connector.

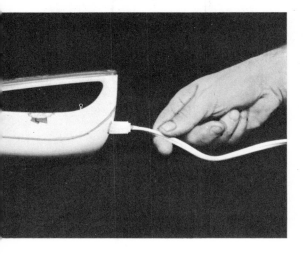

To open the knife, look for body screws. Usually these are of Philips or cross-head type and require well-fitting X-type screwdriver. Turn the latter carefully to avoid damage to the threads.

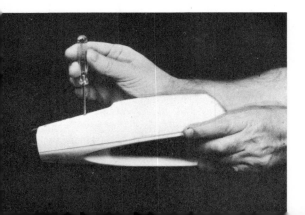

WHEN the electric knife first appeared on the market it was regarded by many people merely as a conversation piece or a status symbol. However, anyone who has owned and used one for any length of time swears by it as a practical addition to the kitchen or the dining room.

Basically, the device consists of a compact but powerful little motor, a gear drive that converts the rotary motion of the motor's shaft to a reciprocating (back and forth) motion, and a knife that is actually a pair of blades. One of the blades is stationary and the other jigs back and forth a fraction of an inch. The edges are serrated, and they bite their way through the toughest meats (and some bones, too!) with surprising ease. You only have to hold the appliance steadily and press down with it lightly.

In a typical knife the motor uses an Alnico permanent magnet field with a conventional armature and commutator. It looks a little small for a 115-volt motor, and investigation reveals that it actually works on about 50 volts DC although it is plugged into a regular 115-volt AC line. The answer to this seeming contradiction is that the circuit includes a tiny rectifier that changes the AC to DC and at the same time reduces the voltage.

The knife shown in the illustrations split conveniently into two sections when the body screws were removed, and the entire mechanism was laid bare. The two brushes that bear on the commutator are readily accessible for inspection or replacement, and the commutator itself can be cleaned in a minute with a small strip of fine sandpaper held against it as it is turned by hand.

In common with other motor-operated appliances that are used only for short periods, electric knives generally do not require lubrication as part of their maintenance. If there are oil holes near the ends of the shaft, apply light oil very sparingly . . . as small a drop as possible.

The control switch on most knives has two positions: On as long as the switch button is kept down with a finger, and on without finger pressure once the button is set about a quarter of a turn to the right.

The line cord is generally loose and plugs in near the back of the handle. A caution: When using the knife, drape the cord behind you, well away from the blades. If the latter hit the cord they most likely will go part of the way through before the dead short-circuit on the wires blows the fuse or circuit breaker in the line. •

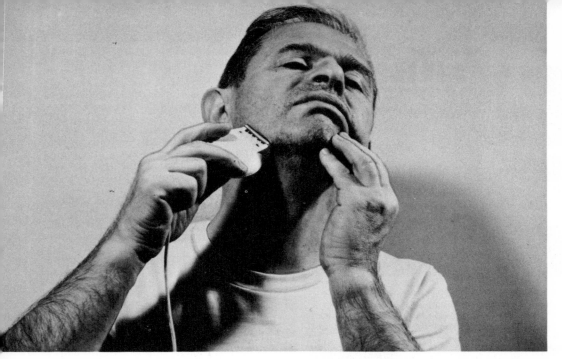

An electric razor cuts hairs closely without gashing the skin. Keep the hands, cord and razor dry.

ELECTRIC RAZORS

They're noisy but effective, and they'll keep buzzing if you keep 'em clean.

IN MANY homes these days the raucous buzzing of father's electric razor is mother's signal to get up and start the coffee. The noise made by this little appliance is probably the only strike against it. It eliminates shaving cream and gashed skin, saves the cost of blades, and leaves the face clean and dry.

By no means an exclusive convenience for men, the electric shaver, in smaller and more delicate designs, has also been adopted enthusiastically by women for removing fuzz from their legs.

These razors use two general forms of motive power: vibrator and motor. The basic vibrator is virtually a refined household buzzer. Alternating current from the house line passes through an electromagnet, near the ends of which is suspended an iron bar called an armature. As the AC varies in strength and direction, it attracts the armature and releases it in rhythm with these changes. The armature is linked to one set of small cutting blades, usually shaped like a comb, which is interleaved with a fixed set. The head of the razor is pressed against the hair, and this is snipped off as it gets trapped between the movable and fixed blades. The actual range of movement is very small; about a hair's breadth, to use an appropriate expression!

In the second type a small motor might agitate the blades, or it might drive rotary cutters.

Some razors have means of adjusting the depth of cut to suit the beard, the condition of the skin and the appearance the user wishes to obtain.

Keep 'Em Clean

If a man has a heavy beard and shaves daily, little bunches of hair are bound to accumulate in the razor mechanism. They can readily reduce the cutting action to the point where the head of the device merely rubs over the skin. For this reason frequent cleaning, *dry*, is highly important. A tiny brush is packed with most razors; use it! Some heads can be disassembled quickly for a thorough scrubbing; others take a bit of doing.

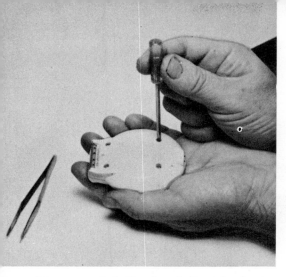

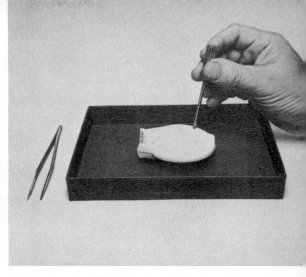

Many razors look like clam shells, and split open like them. As they normally require frequent internal inspection, they are usually constructed to come apart easily. Look for small body screws.

This is one way to keep screws and various other small parts from getting lost: open the razor in a shallow box, preferably of contrasting color. Tweezers (left) are invaluable for replacing parts.

With one half of the clam shell removed, the entire insides of the razor can be examined closely. Small prongs, bottom, are for line connector. Note particularly the fit of armature to cutters.

In this razor none of the components are actually fastened to the body. They merely fit into molded ribs in the two halves of the clam, and become secure only when the latter are screwed together.

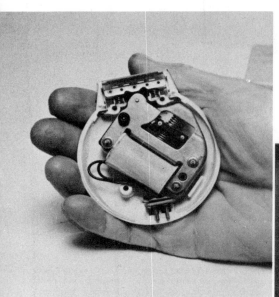

Since all electric razors connect to the 115-volt house line and most shaving is done over or near a sink, which is an electrical "ground," make very, very sure that the hands, the razor and the cord are all thoroughly dry.

Almost all cords are of the detachable type, which makes them easy to roll up and pack with the shavers in their boxes. The connector that goes into base of the razor is usually a rather small, thin one, with the wire molded into it. As is the case with heavier cords made for irons, grills and the like, these cannot be repaired. If the small plug becomes damaged, there's no choice but to buy a whole new cord.

Some razors are built like fine watches. If you want to take one apart to see what makes it buzz, remove screws carefully and make mental notes of where the parts fit. •

Dust off the keyboard before and after machine is used and it will stay clean and pleasant to use.

ELECTRIC TYPEWRITERS

Keep a machine clean and lubricated and it will always write well.

ONCE a status symbol for the secretaries of big-shot business executives, the electric typewriter is now just another household appliance. It is probably the most popular—and useful—of all the gifts wished on high-school graduates.

Full-size office machines are very expensive; in the neighborhood of about $500 and up, mostly up. The new portables, however, are much more reasonable, and also more convenient. They are only slightly larger than manual portables but appreciably heavier because of the extra machinery in them. You wouldn't want to lug one around for an hour, but you can carry it in and out of a car or up and down

Keep an unused paint brush near a typewriter and wield it frequently to remove erasures and dust. Turn the machine to this position, so that dirt will fall away from it instead of into the keys.

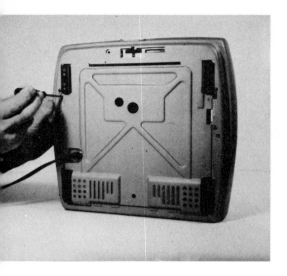

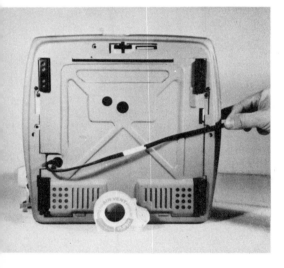

Inside machine should be kept just as clean as outside. Remove fluff with paint brush. Examine drive mechanism for bearings, and use thin oil cn them very sparingly. Motor is at lower left.

A damaged line cord can make case of typewriter alive electrically and dangerous to the touch. Ordinary adhesive tape is excellent for covering worn spots. It is strong, and very good insulator.

stairs, when necessary, without any strain.

The electric machine gets its muscle from a small, high-speed motor that turns the equivalent of a compact flywheel. When you touch a key some of the kinetic energy of the wheel is used to release the actual strike bar, the end of which presses the letter to the ribbon and the paper beneath. It doesn't make any difference whether you just flick the key or tromp on it; the impression made on the paper is the same.

The motor mechanism is usually rather complicated, and the best thing to do with it is to leave it alone except for inspection for possible loose screws and for cleaning. Cleaning, in fact, is the keynote to type-writer maintenance, according to the manufacturers. Most trouble is caused by accumulations of bits of paper mixed with rubbings from erasers. The latter are of course abrasive, and in time can raise hob with bearings.

Excessive oil is also bad, because it holds this rubbish. Some lubrication of bearings and joints is necessary, but tiny drops will do a better job than a wholesale spraying.

As in many other appliances, it's the line cord that usually gives trouble long before the typewriter itself develops any. There isn't much bottom clearance on some machines, and the wire can readily be mashed by their weight. •

FLASHLIGHTS & BATTERIES

They carry their own electricity and are independent of power lines.

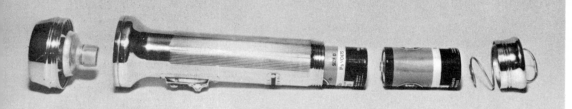

In this style of 2-cell flashlight both ends of the case unscrew. At left is bulb and reflector assembly. At right is opening for the batteries. Spring in cap keeps the latter in tight contact for flow of power.

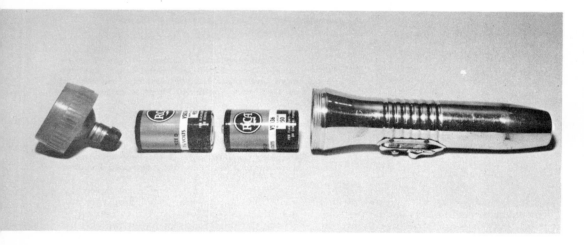

In this style only the bulb assembly comes away from the case; the batteries are dropped into the latter from the top. If they ever bulge because of leakage removal becomes virtually impossible.

IS AN ordinary flashlight considered an electrical appliance? If you're ever caught in the house without one when the electric service fails (for instance, during a storm) you'll learn quickly that it's a mighty useful little "appliance." And it's more than an emergency aid. It's also great for helping to find coins, buttons, jewelry and other small objects that annoyingly roll under furniture or into other dark spots.

If there are children in the house, and a parent wants to go to the bathroom or indulge in a midnight snack in the kitchen without turning on room lights, a flashlight lights the way without awakening anyone.

By far the most widely used flashlight is

the cylindrical type that works on two dry cells of the "D" size. A slightly smaller model uses two "C" cells, which are a bit smaller than the "D." The light from the two are the same, but for about the same initial cost and battery maintenance the larger model is favored because the "D" cells last much longer than the "C."

The secret of long battery life is to keep the light on only when it is absolutely necessary. Conventional dry batteries are intended only for intermittent service, and their voltage drops off rather rapidly if they are kept on too long. However, they have an interesting characteristic; given even short periods of rest, they recuperate quickly. Eventually, the chemicals and other materials in them that generate the electricity will be exhausted, and then replacement is in order.

If batteries are not too far gone it is possible to revive them up, to a point, but for what the "charger" costs you can keep yourself in fresh cells for ten years, without the bother.

Battery Types Compared

For flashlight purposes there is no real advantage in buying the much more expensive dry cells of the alkaline or mercury type. The alkaline is intended for toys and other devices that require much heavier current than that of a flashlight bulb. The mercury is intended particularly for transistor radio sets and other "solid-state" electronic gear that take relatively small currents but are kept on for long periods.

"Dry" cells aren't dry at all, but contain a definitely damp paste-like mixture of chemicals. This goo has a tendency to expand and to leak through the thin zinc body of the battery. When this happens the cells usually become so tightly jammed inside the case of the flashlight that they cannot be forced free without actually wrecking the case.

Most American brand-name batteries have leak-proof cases, but many imported cells lack this feature. They're cheap, but they need to be checked frequently. If they show any signs of a white discharge throw them away, right away.

Any time you open a flashlight to inspect it, brighten up the top and bottom contacts of the cells with sandpaper or emery cloth or any other abrasive that happens to be on hand. Do the same for the center contact of the bulb. This simple treatment often revives a seemingly dying pair of batteries and makes the bulb shine again.

A new flashlight cell measures 1.5 volts;

two in series, as used in a flashlight, thus develop 3 volts. Yet the miniature bulb designed for a two-cell light is rated at 2.3 or 2.4 volts. Why doesn't it burn out quickly? Further, why do most bulbs actually outlast many sets of batteries? The answers lie in the fact that the voltage of conventional dry cells starts to fall off quite soon after a "load" is placed on them; in this case it's the bulb. The reduction is fractional, but it's enough to bring the temperature of the bulb's filament below the melting point.

Most chemical actions are slowed down by cold. Dry cells are definitely affected,

A new cell should measure 1½ volts on low-range DC scale of a VOM. If light dims, check out both cells. Sometimes only one is poor, about 1.1 v., while the other still has lots of energy left.

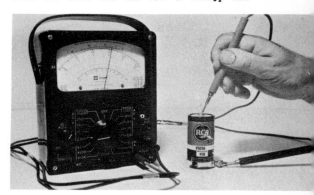

Size comparison of "D" flashlight cell, left, and "C" size, right. Both generate 1.5 volts, but the larger one naturally lasts longer and is a better buy at 18 cents against 13 for the "C" cell.

Before discarding batteries if light grows dark try this simple stunt of cleaning all contacts. It often removes slight chemical corrosion that introduces resistance to the flow of electricity.

In most flashlights bulb has prefocused filament and flanged base and fits in plastic holder that screws over end of reflector. Examine occasionally and clean contacts. Standard bulb is PR-2.

The equivalent of two "D" cells stacked at left, the one-piece battery at the right is a unique storage cell with built-in charger. It produces a steady light and can be re-used indefinitely.

When the top of the storage battery is unscrewed, the insulated end of the case can be seen to have two prongs just like those on conventional line plug. They connect to internal charger and battery.

The battery recharges overnight when it is merely plugged into 115-volt AC outlet. Charge current is small and there is little danger of overcharging. Battery is of the nickel-cadmium type.

Having the same dimensions as two "D" cells, chargeable battery fits accurately in standard flashlight. It is sealed and leakproof and it can be left in flashlight for long periods without bulging.

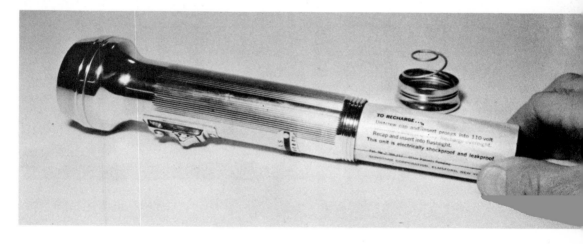

but usually not permanently. A flashlight in a car in an unheated garage during the winter might just about light, but keep it in the house for a few hours and it will come back to life.

Rechargeable Batteries

If you use a flashlight a great deal it might pay to invest in some of the interest-ing new sealed nickel-cadmium storage batteries in the same size and shape as ordinary batteries. What makes them interesting is that they have their own chargers built right into their cases! Unscrew the top and you find a pair of prongs exactly like those of a line plug. Plug them into any AC outlet and overnight a battery that was all spent is again full of pep. •

SMALL TABLE LAMPS

Using automobile bulbs, they offer good high-intensity illumination.

Fractured, but not a hopeless case. The plastic hinge joining the reflector and the top arm gave way, and the bulb shattered. The whole assembly felt loose; the decision was to open it for a look.

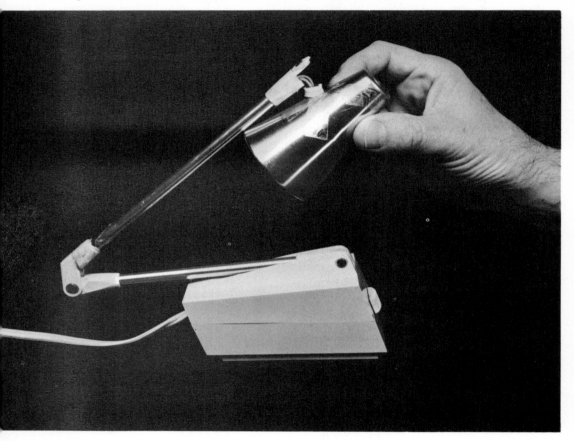

SMALL LAMPS about the size of a teacup have become very popular because they concentrate a lot of light into a small area and are therefore effective for reading of books, working on intricate pieces of equipment, etc. What's different about them? Well, ordinary table lamps use screw-base bulbs that work directly off the 115-volt house line. The "minis" use bayonet-base 14-volt *automobile* bulbs that work off step-down transformers in the base of the lamp assembly.

Some lamps have "high-low" switches that give two intensities of illumination. The lamp voltage in "high" is slightly

above normal, in "low" slightly below. The lamp will run cooler and last much longer in low, as might be expected.

A common complaint about the minis is that the bulbs burn out too soon. This is probably due to the desire of some manufacturers to make their lamps seem brighter than their competitors'; they achieve this end simply by boosting the transformer voltage. The bulbs are brighter, sure enough, but at the expense of highly increased temperature and much reduced life.

Keep a few spares on hand. A burn-out is sure to occur just when you are all curled

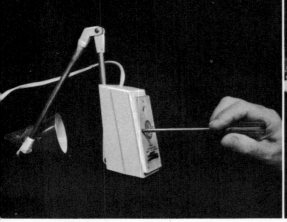

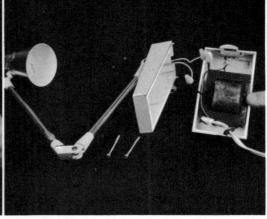

Only fasteners in sight were two screws of the Philips-head type. These were very tight but they yielded to X-point screwdriver that fit snugly. Screws had been threaded directly into plastic.

Secret of the mini lamp is revealed when case is pried open. A transformer (dark object at right) steps house line down to about 14 volts, more or less. On-off switch is in circuit to wall outlet.

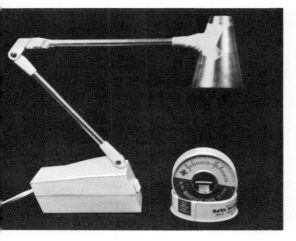

Reassembled and repaired, lamp is as good as new—almost. Reflector is fastened securely to arm with ordinary adhesive tape from family medicine chest. No more hinge action, but plenty of light.

Standard bulb for small lamps is single-contact bayonet base automobile type, General Electric No. 93 or equivalent. Short pins near bottom of base lock it in socket after glass is turned slightly.

up and start to read—so keep them handy.

Automobile bulbs are identified by number. The most widely used one seems to be the General Electric 93.

Most of the troubles that develop with these little lamps is physical. Because they are small and relatively light they can be upset rather readily. The one shown in the illustrations was accidentally pushed off a night table, and the reflector head broke away at the plastic hinge where it joins one of the two adjustable arms. Cement failed to hold the fracture, but a tight bandage of ½-inch adhesive tape restored the lamp to usefulness.

To remove a burned-out bulb, press down on the glass body and at the same time turn it slightly to the left; it will then pop out into your fingers. To install a replacement, put it into the socket and turn it loosely to the right until you feel it drop slightly. Press down and turn a little more to engage the pins in the base of the lamp with the slots in the socket.

In most mini lamps the step-down transformer is sealed in the base and in some models it can get pretty warm after long periods of use. This is no cause for alarm as long as you can touch the base without being scorched. •

Above, a sign of impending danger is torn, worn insulation on the cord at the point it rubs against the lamp base. New cord makes neater repair.

An old unused lamp can be restored to serviceability if it is cleaned up and a new, colorful cord added as shown.

RE-CORDING A LAMP

It will look neater and will be safer to use with a new length of wire.

THE flexible cords of table and floor lamps usually show the first signs of wear at the point where they emerge from the base. If there is any leeway in the wire, sometimes it can be pushed into or pulled out of its hole, taped over, and then put back into place. If the rest of the cord is also damaged in any way, it's better sense in most cases to take out the old cord and put in a completely new one. A typical job on a table lamp is shown in detail in the photo sequence.

Before undertaking this work, consider also the idea of making the new cord considerably longer than the old one. A long cord offers more flexibility in the placement of the lamp and eliminates the need for an extension cord. Most original wires run to six feet. Doubling the length is about right for most home applications.

Also examine the line plug for signs of wear. As a minimum, clean the prongs with sandpaper or emery cloth and make all surfaces bright and shiny. •

Remove the shade for safekeeping; it's obviously held in place with a decorative nut or stud, which unscrews readily. Following this, obviously, the bulb is removed and then actual repair work begins.

Next, snip off the old wire at the base of the lamp. Save good sections for other uses. Below right, to disassemble socket look for word "press" on shell near switch. Insert blade of screwdriver, twist slightly, then press end of socket upward. This opens the toothed joint between the halves of lamp socket.

 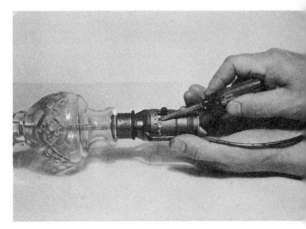

Next, remove old section of wire, inspect and clean socket, and tighten small screws inside shell as needed.

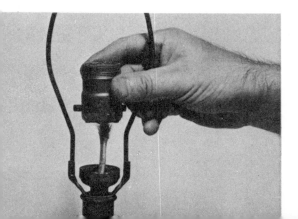 

Next, check fit of socket and shade holder on neck of lamp; twist to right to tighten. Then, below right, feed the length of the new wire through the fixed part of the socket, down through base of the lamp.

 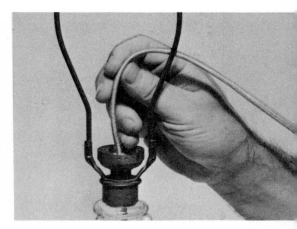

Separate ends of new wire, remove insulation, scrape clean and tighten wires under two screws of the socket shell. Then (below right) from the bottom pull wire down carefully till socket is in position.

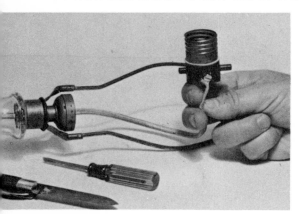 

Now snap other sections of socket back into position; start it at a slight angle and then squeeze along the bottom. Finally, protect new wire where it passes through base with ordinary white adhesive tape.

 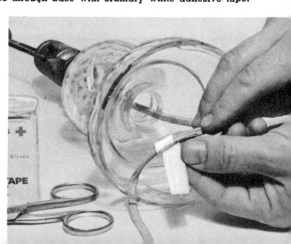

FILM SLIDE PROJECTORS

Keep them dust-free and pictures on the screen will be spotless.

Two popular types of film slide projectors using rotary magazines. The one at top is of flat design, and magazine sits horizontally. In the other, magazine slides vertically into one side of the case.

THE WORD "projector" to most people used to mean "movie projector," but nowadays it is more likely to represent "slide projector." This is because of the popularity of Kodak's Instamatic cameras, which use an absolutely foolproof drop-in film cartridge and a four-sided flash cube. The combination produces color slides (and also color prints) of remarkable quality.

Slides require a projector, but this is not expensive and is a very good investment because slides are much cheaper than color prints on paper and their projected images can be blown up on a screen to spectacular dimensions.

Slide projectors are rather simple and require very little maintenance. The major repair, when a machine stops working, is usually nothing more than the replacement of a burned out lamp. All projection lamps run very hot, some so hot, in fact, that the glass envelopes (as the bulbs are called) often develop bulges. However, they rarely burst because all but the smallest projectors have cooling fans that come on when the lamps are turned on.

In addition to a fan, most projectors have additional protection for the slides in the form of a disc of special heat-absorbent glass positioned between the lamp and the condensing lenses. This glass puzzles many people because it is perfectly flat and ob-

viously cannot help to concentrate the light on the film, as the condensers do.

Lamps have a nasty habit of burning out just as people start to show their slides of Europe or of their children. A spare should always be on hand, and the best place to keep it is right in the case of the projector.

The base of most lamps is similar to that of radio tubes. It is keyed in such a manner that it can be inserted in its socket in only one direction, and then its pre-focused filament is positioned correctly in relation to the projector's optical system.

Dust Is The Problem

Like other electrical appliances that operate in a hot, dry condition, slide projectors attract a lot of dust out of the air of seemingly clean rooms. It does no harm, but if it is allowed to accumulate on the condensing lenses between the lamp and the film and on the projection lens itself it can give the images on the screen a slightly fuzzy appearance. For this reason frequent cleaning is advisable. Some photographers make a habit of blowing out their projectors every time they set them up, and even of removing the lenses and wiping them lightly with soft facial tissues.

The usual precautions about protecting line cords and other wires should of course be observed. The cables used with some

Top section of case appears to be solid, but it snaps open easily. The slot in the center, above the round opening for the rotary magazine, is intended for single slides. Lens is at right end.

With top cover removed, below, left, entire system is exposed and can be dusted or blown out without disturbing anything. Bulb is in left compartment, condensing lenses and projection lens at right.

Top of lamp is covered by metal strip to protect eyes of user if he checks the operation of projector with current on. It is held in place by friction and snaps loose readily without using any tools.

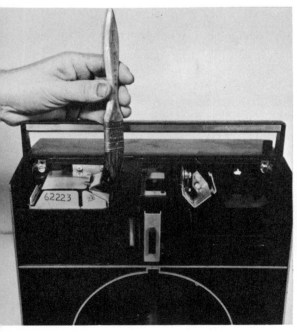

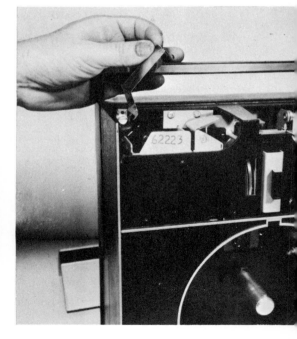

Lifting of shield leaves lamp accessible. Trick in removing it is to grasp firmly with the fingers and to PULL straight up without twisting. It has a keyed base, not usual bayonet or screw type. Projection lamp looks like radio tube, with pins in base. Top is painted to minimize upward glare. Filament is extremely bright and can cause temporary eye discomfort if it is viewed too closely.

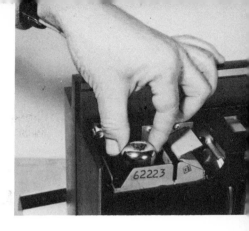

In flat-style projector, a coin-opening compartment is provided for storage of line cord, other accessories. In this view the machine is upside down. Grill, right, is exhaust area for cooling fan.

Always check the spare projection lamp immediately after buying it and before putting it away. Glass envelope diameters might vary a little, but base pins and heights of filaments must be exact.

A great gadget for blowing dust out of projector (or any similar machine that must be kept clean) is a plastic squeeze bottle with a small hole in its cap. First wash out interior and dry thoroughly.

remote control devices are rather thin and merit special attention.

The commonest operating fault with projectors is mechanical rather than electrical. This is jamming of the slides in the feed mechanism. Often it is due to bent or twisted slides, which simply cannot be accommodated in the narrow space of its carrier. If the trouble persists even with flat, undamaged slides, the machine itself is basically bad.

Jamming can be so annoying that no one should buy any projector without an iron-bound guarantee from the dealer (NOT the manufacturer) that he will take it back if it is not satisfactory. One way to get this protection automatically is to take the machine on a charge account. Run a couple of magazines of good slides and if even one sticks repack the whole thing and bounce it back to the seller. If it jams once you can be pretty certain that it will jam again. •